INTRODUCTORY FOODS
A Laboratory Manual of Food Preparation and Evaluation

Fourth Edition

Mary L. Morr
Associate Professor, Emeritus
Michigan State University

Theodore F. Irmiter
Professor
Kent State University

8 August 1989

To - Laura & Brad

May your cakes never
fall or your pudding never
be lumpy. Bon Appetite

Doris & Ted.

Macmillan Publishing Company
New York
Collier Macmillan Publishers
London

Macmillan Publishing Company
866 Third Avenue, New York, New York 10022

Collier Macmillan Canada, Inc.

ISBN 0-02-384130-3

Printing: 3 4 5 6 7 8   Year: 7 8 9 0 1 2

Preface to the Fourth Edition

From the Preface to the First Edition,

> "The material included in this manual has been selected because it illustrated the chemical and physical principles governing the preparation of food products in the home, in a restaurant, or in a factory. The teaching of skills has been *subordinated* to the development of an understanding of the principles. Emphasis has also been placed on the recognition and evaluation of the quality of the food products that have been prepared."

Because of this primary objective, we have limited the number of recipes included, especially in the early lessons where the student is engaged in getting "the feel" of preparing food and at the same time starting to learn the intricacies of food evaluation. We are convinced that too many products included in one lesson will make the evaluations less reliable and , even more important, will serve to obscure the application of principles. The temptation to add more recipes is great but we have resisted. We have selected and maintained the order of the work because by starting with baked products the student will be exposed early to such important concepts as hydration, coagulation, and gelatinization.

We have retained the expanded use of metric measures introduced in the Third Edition although there does not seem to be any movement toward adoption of the metric system in the United States. A unit on "Microwave Cooking" was also introduced in the Third Edition and in this new edition we have cross-referenced all of the recipes in the microwave lesson with the similar recipes prepared by the conventional method; we feel this will help the student to better understand and compare the two methods of cooking.

Two new units of work have been added to this edition. A unit on "Crystallization: Water (Frozen Desserts)" is a logical extension of "Crystallization: Sugar (Candies)." Also added is a unit on "Appliances for Food Preparation." The many small appliances now available help to achieve work simplification and energy conservation. These are two worthwhile objectives that fit into our philosophy of food preparation.

M.L.M.
T.F.I.

Contents

Objectives of the Laboratory Experience   1

Laboratory Conduct and Responsibilities   2

Evaluation of Food Products   4

Metric Conversion   9

Tables of Equivalents   11

Temperatures Used in Food Preparation   12

Introduction and Demonstration   13

Basic Terms and Concepts   19

Descriptive Terms Used in Judging Characteristics of Baked Products   20

Muffins   21

Baking Powder Biscuits   29

Yeast Breads   37

Butter Type Cakes   45

Cream Puffs and Popovers   57

Fats and Oils   67

Pie Pastry: Fruit Pies   71

Deep-Fat Frying   83

Starch   89

Rice, Paste Products, and Cereals   97

Milk   104

Cheese   110

Eggs and Custards   117

Egg Foams   123

Starch-Egg Combinations   133

Meat—Tender Cuts: Dry Heat Methods   137

Meat—Less Tender Cuts: Moist Heat Methods   145

Fish and Shellfish   157

Vegetables   167

Dried Legumes   182

Fruits   186

Salads   201

Salad Dressings   211

Gelatin   215

Beverages   224

Crystallization: Sugar (Candies)   231

Crystallization: Water (Frozen Desserts)   240

Microwave Cooking   248

Appliances for Food Preparation   258

Appendix A: Evaluation Sheets   264

Appendix B: Summary Outline Sheets   295

Index: Recipe   307

Index: Subject   311

Objectives of the Laboratory Experiences

*1. Illustrate the principles discussed in lecture and demonstrate the application of these principles in the actual preparation of food.

2. Acquaint the student with acceptable method(s) for the preparation of selected food products including microwave cooking.

3. Acquaint the student with established standards for food products.

**4. Acquaint the student with one method for evaluating the quality of food products for compliance with established standards.

5. Give the student the opportunity to observe the effect of certain manipulative procedures on the quality of selected food products.

6. Acquaint the student with acceptable sanitary standards and procedures for handling food products and to impress upon the student the absolute necessity for adherence to these standards.

7. Foster a professional attitude in each student toward his work.

*It is recognized the same principles apply to small portions (2-4 servings) as well as to large quantities (100–400 servings). In the preparation of large quantities, *additional* principles may be involved; these principles would not be applicable to the smaller portions.

**Other techniques for recording observations will be used occasionally.

Laboratory Conduct and Responsibilities

PERSONAL CONDUCT

1. Do not chew gum, eat candy, or drink beverages other than water during the laboratory period.
2. Do not read magazines or newspapers during the laboratory period.
3. Do not use work units, supply tables, or window ledges as seats.
4. Each student is responsible for washing his own equipment. He must also keep work surfaces and sinks clean.
5. Each student must assist in general housekeeping of the laboratory.

PERSONAL HYGIENE

1. Wash hands with soap before working with food. Do not dry hands on dish towels.
2. Wash hands after using a handkerchief, before handling foods again.
3. Avoid touching the hair or face while working with food; wash hands after each contact.
4. Hair must *not* be combed in the laboratory at any time. Hair combing should be done before the student enters the laboratory.

FOOD HANDLING

1. Spoons and/or rubber spatulas used for blending or stirring food ingredients are *not* to be licked.
2. Use a special spoon or fork for sampling any food product to test for degree of doneness or for amount of seasoning.
3. Any spoon or fork placed in the mouth *must be washed* before being used for further food sampling.
4. Observe the special instructions for preparation of fresh foods where indicated in a lesson.

DISHWASHING

Preparation for Washing

1. Rinse and/or soak soiled utensils immediately after use.
   a. *Greasy pans:*
      (1) Wipe pans with paper toweling to absorb grease.
      (2) Put detergent in the pan with *hot* water for soaking.

    b. *Sugar syrups or similar:*
       Soak in *hot* water.
    c. *Protein foods:*
       (1) Soak in *cold* water.
       (2) Rinse egg beaters in cold tap water *immediately* after use.
    d. *Starchy foods:*
       Soak in *cold* water.

2. If a food scorches or burns in a cooking pan, remove pan *immediately* from heat:
    a. Transfer food quickly into another container.
    b. If a cooking utensil is glass or enamel, allow it to cool before adding hot water. Place the utensil over low heat for 10–15 minutes after hot water has been added. *Caution:* Oven glassware cannot be put over direct heat.
3. Any large pieces of food material which have soaked free from the cooking pan should be placed in the garbage. Dry flour *must not* be scraped into any sink.
4. Use rubber or plastic spatula or paper toweling to remove loosened food material from utensils.
5. Rinse dishes with hot water. Stack for washing with detergent.

Washing Procedure

1. Run several inches of hot (120°F or 49°C) water into sink or dishpan.
2. Add enough detergent to form a suds which remains sudsy during the dishwashing.
3. Place several of the rinsed dishes in the hot, soapy water. Wash with a clean brush or dishcloth.
4. Rinse the washed dishes in ample *hot* water (150°F or 66°C) in order to remove the soapy film.
5. Place the rinsed dishes in dish drainers. Dry all utensils with a clean, dry dish towel. Dish towels should not be carried about on the shoulder or used for drying hands.
6. All pieces of equipment must be thoroughly dry before being returned to storage.
7. Dry dish pans, dish drainers, and drainer mats before returning to their storage area.

Care of Sinks

1. *Each student* is expected to assume responsibility for the use and care of sinks.
2. No food material is to be discarded in sinks that have no disposal units. Place refuse either in disposal sinks or pans for garbage.
3. Aluminum pans leave gray streaks on porcelain sinks. Use care in handling pans in the sink. At the end of dishwashing use cleanser to scour aluminum stains off the porcelain.
4. Each person is responsible for washing out his sink with hot, sudsy water at the end of the dishwashing. Rinse suds away with ample hot water.
5. Leave water taps clean and dry.

Use and Care of Dishcloths and Dish Towels

1. Dish towels are to be used for drying dishes *only.*
2. Dishcloths are to be wrung dry at the end of the dishwashing period.
3. Handle used towels and dishcloths as directed by the instructor.

CHECK-OUT OF UNITS

1. Each student is responsible for returning all equipment to its proper location in the unit. Each piece of equipment should be cleaned and dried before it is returned to its storage area.
2. Instructors may check out units before students leave the laboratory at the end of the day's work.

Evaluation of Food Products

INTRODUCTION

To accomplish the objectives of studying the principles of food preparation and their application to the actual preparation of food, food products will be carefully prepared and then will be carefully evaluated in a systematic manner to determine if the characteristics of the product meet the established standards of quality. Every food product will be "right" for the treatment it has received; for example, a burned cake has obviously been baked at too high an oven temperature for the recommended baking time, or it has been in the oven for too long a time at the proper baking temperature. Evaluation of the characteristics which influence the quality of the prepared product is seldom as simple as the observations for the burned cake.

It is true, "the proof of the pudding is in the eating." Difficulties begin in attempting to determine the quality of the pudding because the evaluation of any food product is complex. One might take a bite of the pudding and decide, "I like it" or "I dislike it," but even this simple decision is quite complex. Furthermore, such a decision tells very little about the quality of the product.

The simple decision "I like it" is based on a combination of ethnic, cultural, religious, psychological, and physiological factors. Most of these factors probably were not consciously considered in making the decision, but nevertheless have influenced the decision. Once the existence of all these factors has been recognized, a conscious effort can be exerted to base the evaluation on only the pertinent factors.

Great progress has been made in the last few years in the procedures and techniques used for evaluation of food products. Tests based on sensory evaluations are *subjective* in nature and may represent personal bias; tests run on machines, however, are *objective* and reflect a minimum of personal bias, although taking data from machines may be influenced by human accuracy. The choice of the type of test to be used is largely dependent on the information desired. One type of test will be used by the food manufacturer who wishes to know how the public will accept a new product he plans to market; an entirely different test would be used by the research worker who is studying the effects of different methods of cooking on muscles of the beef round.

It is beyond the scope of this manual to discuss all of the methods for the evaluation of food products. For the purposes of this manual, one sensory method of evaluation of foods will be presented and developed. This method is based on a systematic evaluation of the physiological factors of sight, feel, aroma, and taste. It takes very considerable skill, developed only through diligent practice, to become proficient in evaluating foods. So that the student can begin to develop this proficiency only this method will be presented. Other methods of sensory evaluation, such as the triangle test, the duo-trio test, paired comparison, ranking, and other more sophisticated tests belong in a more advanced foods course.

QUALITY OF PRODUCTS

A worker carefully following a balanced recipe, accurately measuring ingredients, and diligently carrying out the manipulative procedure will obtain a product that has certain desirable quality characteristics.

Quality characteristics are dependent on the nature and type of food product. Products prepared within the scope of this laboratory outline will usually be evaluated on the characteristics of appearance, texture, tenderness, and flavor.

Appearance includes the shape, size, color, and condition of the outside surface, and in some products (certain baked products and some meats) the interior color.

Texture refers to the nature of the structure of the product. For baked products, texture refers to the size of the gas cells and to the thickness of the cell walls. In meat, texture refers to the size of the muscle fibers and/or the size of the bundles of muscle fibers. In some food products, such as tomato soup and cornstarch pudding, the textural characteristics are referred to as body or consistency.

Flavor of food is the taste and aroma of the food as it is chewed and will be typical of the product being scored. Deviations from the typical flavor are referred to as "off flavors" and may arise from a number of causes.

In some products it may be desirable to evaluate other characteristics such as *tenderness* and *moistness* in baked products and *tenderness* and *juiciness* in meat. *Tenderness* refers to the ease with which a product may be cut, broken, or chewed. These characteristics will be discussed in detail as they are encountered in the various products.

However, a product may not have the characteristics associated with a high quality product and may be something less than an acceptable product. One subjective procedure for determining how closely a product achieves the characteristic of high quality is detailed in the following sections.

GENERAL DESCRIPTION OF THE SELECTED TEST

A scalar scoring procedure will be used for the most part throughout this manual; that is, a numerical value is used to score each of the quality characteristics of the product. Descriptive terms may be used in addition to the assigned numerical score. Study the evaluation sheet which follows this discussion to see the format and how it looks when it is filled out.

This particular procedure has been selected because it aids in meeting the objectives of the course. When properly carried out, the scalar scoring procedure will tell how the product deviates from the standard, by how much it deviates, and will offer a clue as to *why* the product deviates. In this latter instance the scoring procedure shows what happens when the principles of food preparation are improperly applied or ignored.

RATING SCALES

Many different scales have been proposed for scoring food products. Some scales have as few as three points whereas others have as many as one hundred; some scales have all positive numbers whereas others have both positive and negative numbers. If there are too few points on the scale, the scorer cannot be sufficiently discriminating to accurately evaluate the sample. On the other hand, if there are too many points on the scale, the scorer becomes confused and is inclined to guess. The results, in either case, are less accurate than if an appropriate number of points are chosen for the scale.

It has been found that an odd number of points is better than an even number of points on a rating scale. In this way, the mid-point of the scale becomes a neutral point and there are an equal number of points on the good side and on the poor side of the scale. Usually, low numbers signify poor quality whereas high numbers signify good quality. This concept of high numbers indicating high quality will be used in evaluating the food products presented in this manual. Only whole numbers are used. No attempt should be made to assign fractional values as most people do not have a sufficient power of discrimination to justify their use.

LABORATORY PROCEDURE FOR EVALUATION

Each person *must* do his own work: there must not be any talking while foods are being evaluated. Generally class discussion led by the instructor will follow the individual evaluation of the products.

The success of the entire scoring procedure depends on the degree to which the scorer can put himself into the position of an impartial judge. Ethnic, religious, and psychological (personal) prejudices *must* be put aside. The scorer must consciously decide to do a careful evaluation. Diligence in the evaluation of foods is as important as care in the preparation of foods. The person doing the evaluation must develop a "scoring attitude" (i.e., get psyched–up). This requires complete concentration to the evaluation—the setting must be such that there is no interruption while the evaluations are taking place. The student must have a positive attitude toward the whole evaluation process. It would be well to read the admonition— the last paragraph of this section.

Individual evaluation will enable the student to determine how closely the quality characteristics of his product match the desired quality characteristics of the product. Rarely will a high quality product be available for direct comparison with the product being scored. Therefore, the student has the responsibility for learning the described quality characteristics for the various products. The student will be guided in making the judgments necessary for evaluating his product against the described quality characteristics of a high quality product.

Evaluation sheets are included. A sheet will be found at the end of each lesson in the baked products unit. Additional sheets are to be found in Appendix A. The left-hand column of the evaluation sheet lists the quality characteristics to be evaluated. These characteristics may be changed for certain types of products; for example, *juiciness* in addition to *texture* for meats.

In the space at the top of each column the student is to identify the product being evaluated. The visual characteristics (appearance, texture, and so on) are scored first. After the descriptions for the quality characteristics of the high quality product have been read, the decision must be made as to how closely the product characteristics matches the description: if it matches closely, score the product 6 or 7. If the product does not match the description, score it at some lesser value; the farther the product characteristic deviates from the description, the lower the score assigned. Record the numerical score in the small box in the upper left-hand corner. The remainder of the box is used for the descriptive terms justifying or giving validity to the particular numerical score assigned. If the score lies in the range of excellent to good products (7–5) the descriptive terms may be omitted; however, if the score lies in the medium to very poor (4–1), the proper descriptive terms *must* be used. Descriptive terms should be kept brief but clear. Each quality characteristic should be scored in this manner.

For many products the characteristic of "Overall Eating Quality" will be evaluated. This represents the judge's overall estimate of the product and is *not* an average of the scores assigned to all of the other quality characteristics. (Is the product servable to friends and acquaintances? Is the product saleable in a high quality restaurant?)

A word of caution about two sources of error in scoring of foods. First, by being careless, the scorer may miss the differences that should have been detected and, second, the scorer may be hypercritical and mark down deviations that in reality do not exist. One type of error is just as bad as the other.

EXAMPLES

The sample evaluation sheet, page 8, shows how several types of products might be scored.

The muffin did not meet the established quality standards and would be rated a poor product: the numerical values tell that much. The descriptive terms are clues indicating why this muffin was a poor product and, as will be shown later, the terms describe a muffin that has been overmixed.

Note that the characteristic of *tenderness* is not scored for a product like soup.

The tomato soup leaves much to be desired, but the reasons may not be obvious. The fact that the soup is too thin might indicate any of several deviations:

1. Incorrect measurements—too much milk, too much tomato juice, or too little starch.
2. Undercooking—starch not gelatinized.
3. Overcooking—starch hydrolyzed.

However, when all of the other comments are considered, it appears the soup has been undercooked. The first clue is the oily surface, indicating an unstable emulsion due to incomplete gelatinization of the starch. The second clue is the starchy flavor which can be due only to undercooked starch. Other possible causes of the thin consistency cannot be completely ruled out: the cook might have made more than one error!

The pork chop as prepared rated as a high quality product; therefore, the use of descriptive terms is not essential for denoting quality, but the use of descriptive terms emphasizes the desirable characteristics of a high quality product.

The olive green color of the green beans is an indication of the effect of acid on chlorophyll. Volatile acids normally present in the vegetable are trapped within the saucepan when the pan is covered and with the nonvolatile acids react with the green pigment to produce the olive green color. The mushy surface and mushy texture indicate excessive breakdown of cell structure as a result of overcooking.

The Quick Mix Cake must be given a low rating due to the bitter flavor although the appearance, texture, and tenderness scores seem to indicate the cake was a high quality product.

CONCLUSION

Careful evaluation of food products can substantially increase the knowledge and understanding of food preparation. The information obtained by scoring will be in direct proportion to the care and diligence used in carrying out the evaluation.

EVALUATION OF PRODUCTS

Score System

Points	Quality
7	Excellent
6	Very good
5	Good
4	Medium
3	Fair
2	Poor
1	Very poor

Directions:

1. Place the numerical score in the box in the upper left hand corner.
2. Comments should justify the numerical score. Comments must be brief.
3. Evaluation of the food products must be on an *individual* basis.

Products

Quality Characteristic	Muffin		Tomato Soup		Pork Chop		Green Beans		Quick Mix Cake	
Appearance	3	Smooth, shiny, peaked, pale	4	Oily surface	5	Evenly browned	3	Olive green color, surface mushy	6	Even top crust, golden color
Consistency or Texture	2	Tunnels	2	Thin	5	Fine grained	3	Disintegrates in mouth, mushy	6	Fine, even cell structure
Tenderness	3	Tough	1		6	Tender	2	Very soft, little resistance to bite	6	Very little resistance to bite
Flavor	5	Bland; slightly sweet	4	Starchy	6		4	Lacks fresh bean flavor	3	Bitter
Overall Eating Quality	3		3		6		2	Poor	3	Poor flavor
	(Overmixed)		(Starch undercooked)		(Standard)		(Overcooked in closed pan)		(Too much vanilla)	

Metric Conversion

INTRODUCTION

The process of conversion from our customary* system of measurements to the metric system is on a voluntary basis and this has led to different approaches for making the conversion. For a complete discussion of the conversion process, reference is made to the publication, *Think Metric: Handbook for Metric Usage*, published by the American Home Economics Association in 1977. A "soft" conversion is one of vocabulary only; one quart equals 0.946 liter so one cup would contain 236.6 milliliters; fractional measures would derive from this. "Hard" conversion involves a real quantitative measurement change to even metric units such as one liter (1 L); thus a "metric cup" would contain 250 milliliters. "Hard" conversion has required resizing of measuring equipment to standard metric modules. The figures in Table 1 compare these quantitative differences and the resizing is evident in the column marked "hard" conversion. The standards on which resizing have been based were established by a committee of the American National Standards Institute.

TABLE 1

Customary U.S.A.	"Soft" Conversion	"Hard" Conversion
1 cup	236.6 ml	250 ml
1/2 cup	118.3 ml	125 ml
1/3 cup**	78.8 ml	**
1/4 cup	59.1 ml	50 ml

**A measure equivalent to this size is not available in "sets" of measuring devices.

Measuring devices based on both "soft" and "hard" conversion may be purchased for metric measurement of foods in the home.

PROCEDURE AND DISCUSSION

The "hard" conversion procedure has been used in this manual although it does not yield precise, quantitative, equivalent measures; conversion factors which have been used appear in Part I, Table I and Part III in the Tables of Equivalents (see page 11). We have accepted the recommendation on page 11 of *Think Metric: Handbook for Metric Usage*, ". . . metric devices should not be called *cups* or *spoons*"; metric measuring utensils should be referred to as *measures* or *measuring devices*. The system of "hard" conversion does *not* yield a precise mathematical conversion but rather a new system of measurements that embodies the inherent simplicity of the metric system. The two systems, however, do share a common ground in that the 250 milliliter measure has the same 4 to 1 ratio to a liter that one cup has to a quart; this may help to put the two system of measurments into proper perspective.

*Customary measurements are referred to in this manual as U.S.A. measurements.

In selecting metric measurements, care has been taken to be sure the ratio of ingredients will yield a satisfactory product, and that the measurements are practical to make; it is important in the laboratory for the student to be able to measure ingredients quickly and with a minimum of error. In those instances where quantitative differences in the amount of an ingredient indicated that the quality of the product would be affected, the recipe has been carefully tested and the resulting product deemed acceptable.

In addition to the conversion of recipes to metric units, sizes of food pieces, pan sizes, and cooking or baking temperatures have also been converted to metric units. Part III in the Tables of Equivalents (page 11) contains the length measure conversions; temperature conversions appear on the thermometer diagram (page 12).

The volumetric system of measurements is more suited to use in the home; the metric system presented herein does not require basic changes in the techniques of measuring, but only a change in units employed. Gravimetric measuring of ingredients as currently practiced in quantity food preparation will be continued and will need to be converted to metric units of grams and kilograms, a matter which is beyond the scope of this manual.

Either the customary (U.S.A.) or metric measurements may be used with the expectation of obtaining a high quality product, when the recipe is followed carefully. In using metric measures one must learn to "think metric" and resist the strong temptation to make mental conversions from customary units to metric units.

Tables of Equivalents

Discussion material explains why by "hard" conversion 1/4 cup is equal to only 50 ml.

Part I Volumetric Measurements

Table 1 "Hard" conversion as used in this manual

1 cup = 250 ml	1 tablespoon = 15 ml
1/2 cup = 125 ml	1 teaspoon = 5 ml
1/4 cup = 50 ml	1/2 teaspoon = 2 ml
	1/4 teaspoon = 1 ml
	1/8 teaspoon = 0.5 ml

Table 2 "Soft" conversion not used in this manual

1 quart = 946.0 ml (0.946 L)	1/2 cup = 118.3 ml
1 cup = 236.6 ml	1/3 cup = 78.8 ml
	1/4 cup = 59.1 ml

Table 3 Fractional U.S. measurements

1 quart	= 4 cups	1 cup = 8 ounces liquid measure
1 pint	= 2 cups	
1 cup	= 16 tablespoons	
1 tablespoon	= 3 teaspoons	

Part II Gravimetric (Weight) Measurements

16 ounces = 1 pound = 453.6 grams
1 ounce = 28.4 grams

Part III Length Measurements

12 inches = 1 foot = 30.8 cm
1 inch = 2.5 cm

Fractional measures as used in this manual

3/4	inch =	2.0 cm
1/2	inch =	1.3 cm
3/8	inch =	1.0 cm
1/4	inch =	0.6 cm
1/8	inch =	0.3 cm
1/16	inch =	0.2 cm

Part IV Abbreviations (to be memorized)

qt	= quart	lb = pound		L	= liter
pt	= pint	oz = ounce		ml	= milliliter
c	= cup	ft = foot		g	= gram
tbsp	= tablespoon	in = inch		cm	= centimeter
tsp	= teaspoon				

TEMPERATURES USED IN FOOD PREPARATION

	(Degrees Fahrenheit) °F	°C (Degrees Celsius)	
Oven Temperatures:			
Extremely hot oven	525	274	
	500	260	
Very hot oven	475	246	
	450	232	
Hot oven	425	218	(Muffins, biscuits, pie pastry)
	400	205	
Moderate oven	375	190	(Angel and sponge cakes, custards and souffles—set in pan of water; macaroni and cheese—all 350° F).
	350	176	
Slow oven	325	163	
	300	149	(Roasting large roasts of meat, roasting poultry—325° F).
Deep-fat Frying:	395	201	(French-fried potatoes)
	375	190	(Croquettes, onions, eggplant)
	350	177	(Chicken, fish, fritters)
Sugar Cookery:	338	170	(Caramelization of sugar)
	320	160	(Granulated sugar liquifies)
	310	154	(Hard crack—Peanut Brittle)
	290	143	(Soft crack—Taffy, Butterscotch)
	266	130	(Hard ball—Divinity, Marshmallows)
	248	120	(Firm ball—Caramels)
	239	115	(Soft ball—Fudge, Penuche)
	234	112	(Very soft ball—Fondant)
Steam Pressure:	250	121	(15 lbs. pressure at sea level)
	240	115	(10 lbs. pressure at sea level)
	228	109	(5 lbs. pressure at sea level)
Water Temperatures:			
Boiling water	212	100	(0 lbs. pressure at sea level)
Simmering range	210	99	(Bubbles vigorously break on surface)
	185	85	
Scalding	149	65	
Lukewarm	104	40	
Changes in Foods:	214	101	(Coagulation of protein in baked products of low sugar content)
	208	98	(Steep beverages: tea, coffee)
	203	95	(Maximum gelatinization of starch)
	170	77	(End temp. in cooking pork to kill trichinae; well-done beef)
	165	74	
	160	70	(Medium beef; egg yolk and whole egg coagulate)
	149	65	(Complete coagulation egg white; starch begins to gelatinize)
	140	60	(Rare beef)
	125	52	(Coagulation of egg white begins)
	120	49	
	115	46	(Maximum for rehydration of dry yeast)
	104	40	(Optimum activity of rennin enzyme)
	90	33	(Optimum for yeast fermentation)
	60	15	
	45	7	(Maximum temp. for refrigeration)
	40	5	
	35	2	(Optimum temp. for refrigeration)
	32	0	(Freezing temp. of water)
	29	- 1.7	(Cold storage of eggs in shell)
	0	-17.8	(Range for freezer storage of foods)
	-10	-23.3	

Temperature Effect on Bacterial Growth/Survival:

165–140°F (74–60°C) Prevents growth; allows survival.

140–120°F (60–49°C) Some growth occurs; many bacteria survive.

120–60°F (49–15°C) **Danger Zone:**
1) Bacteria grow rapidly.
2) Toxins produced by some bacteria.

60–40°F (15–4°C) Some bacterial growth occurs.

40–32°F (4–0°C) Slow growth of bacteria causing food spoilage.

32–0°F (0° to –18°C) Some bacteria survive freezing. No growth at low temp.

140–40°F (60–4°C) Critical temp. range for food poisoning bacteria.

Introduction and Demonstration

OBJECTIVES

1. To discuss with students expectations from a food preparation laboratory:
   a. from student's viewpoint.
   b. from instructor's viewpoint.
2. To acquaint students with procedural patterns for laboratory sessions.
3. To demonstrate and discuss acceptable methods for measurement of selected ingredients.
4. To acquaint students with selected equipment used in food preparation.
5. To acquaint students with temperatures used in the preparation of food products.
6. To introduce the student to a systematic procedure for the evaluation of the quality of food products.

PRODUCT TO BE PREPARED TO ILLUSTRATE PRINCIPLES

Demonstration by instructor of Methods of Measurement
Muffins

PRINCIPLES

1. Separation of particles of a dry ingredient by sifting, rolling, and/or stirring equalizes the density of the ingredient.
2. Volume measurements may be less accurate than weight measurements.
3. Use of an equivalent measurement may increase accuracy of measurement.
4. High standards of safety and sanitation must be maintained in handling and preparing food.
5. The quality characteristics of food products must be evaluated as objectively as possible.

METHODS OF MEASUREMENT—MUFFINS*

Ingredient	Measurement	Techniques Used
Flour, all-purpose	1 cup *or* 250 ml	
Baking powder	2 teaspoons *or* 10 ml	
Salt	1/2 teaspoon *or* 2 ml	
Sugar	3 tablespoons *or* 45 ml	
Milk	1/2 cup *or* 125 ml	
Egg, blended	2 tablespoons *or* 30 ml	
Liquid shortening**	2 tablespoons *or* 30 ml	

*These measurements will yield 5 or 6 muffins. Use Muffin Method on page 22 for combining ingredients.

**Demonstrate techniques of measuring solid fat at beginning of Baking Powder Biscuit lesson on page 30.

CHARACTERISTICS OF HIGH QUALITY MUFFINS

Appearance: Top crust has a cauliflower-like appearance; is rather rough or pebbled; is golden brown.

Texture: Uniform distribution of gas holes; gas holes may be fairly large; the cell walls are of medium thickness.

Tenderness: Very little resistance when bitten and chewed.

Flavor: Usually bland or very slightly sweet.

Eating Quality: Overall satisfaction in serving and eating this product is high.

EVALUATION OF PRODUCTS

Name: _____

Date: _____

Score System

Points	Quality
7	Excellent
6	Very good
5	Good
4	Medium
3	Fair
2	Poor
1	Very poor

Directions:

1. Place the numerical score in the box in the upper left hand corner.
2. Comments should justify the numerical score. Comments must be brief.
3. Evaluation of the food products must be on an *individual* basis.

Products

Quality Characteristic					
Appearance					
Consistency or Texture					
Tenderness					
Flavor					
Overall Eating Quality					

15

REVIEW QUESTIONS

Methods of Measurement
1. a. Why is flour usually sifted before it is measured?
    b. Under what circumstances is flour *not* sifted before measuring?
2. a. What types of dry ingredients are not sifted before measuring?
    b. State the reason for not sifting each ingredient listed in 2a.
3. Why must the mark on the glass measuring cup be at eye level?
4. How would you measure 1/8 teaspoon cream of tartar?
5. How would you measure 1/8 cup of milk? Of flour?
6. How would you measure 4 tablespoons of sugar? Of flour? Why?
7. How would you measure 3 teaspoons of baking powder? Why?
8. How would you measure 1/6 cup?
9. How would you measure 1/2 cup of brown sugar?
10. How would you measure 3/8 cup of solid fat?
11. Triple all quantities in the following recipe and indicate how each ingredient would be correctly measured.

MUFFIN RECIPE

Ingredient	Amount	3X Amount	How Measured
Flour, all-purpose	1 cup		
Baking powder	2 teaspoons		
Salt	1/2 teaspoon		
Milk	1/2 cup		
Egg	2 tablespoons		
Liquid shortening	2 tablespoons		
Sugar	3 tablespoons		

12. How would you measure 25 milliliters of sugar? Of milk? Of vegetable oil?
13. How would you measure 45 milliliters sugar? 50 milliliters of sugar? 150 milliliters of sugar?
14. How would you measure 0.5 milliliter of salt?
15. How would you measure 30 milliliters of milk?
16. How would you measure 1.5 liters of flour?

17. Reduce all quantities by one-fourth in the following recipe. Indicate how each ingredient would be correctly measured.

MUFFIN RECIPE—METRIC MEASURES

Ingredient	Amount	One-fourth Amount	How Measured
Flour, all-purpose	1 L		
Baking powder	40 ml		
Salt	8 ml		
Milk	500 ml		
Liquid shortening	120 ml		
Sugar	180 ml		

Safety and Sanitation
1. a. Why are uniforms required for each student in the laboratory?
   b. Why are hairnets or caps required?
2. a. Why are pans and utensils used for preparing protein foods and starchy foods rinsed in cold water? (*Note:* An understanding of the terms *coagulation* and *gelatinization* is required.)
   b. Why is hot water used to rinse pans which contained:
      (1) Fats (after most of fat has been wiped out with paper toweling)?
      (2) Sugar or sugar syrups?
3. a. What is the relationship between water temperature and destruction of micro-organisms?
   b. What are the two functions of soap in washing dishes?
4. What is the proper water temperature for:
   a. Washing dishes?
   b. Rinsing dishes?

Evaluation of Foods
1. List some of the personal factors which may influence evaluation of a food product.
2. a. Name the two general types of tests which may be used to evaluate a food product.
   b. Which of these two tests embodies the least personal bias?
3. List the factors to be considered or steps to be taken by the individual if his evaluation of a food product is to be as objective as possible.

Basic Terms and Concepts

This is a basic vocabulary for food study. A good working knowledge of these terms and concepts is essential for an understanding of the changes taking place in food preparation. Students need to learn these terms early to be able to read and understand textbooks. Refer to a textbook and the American Home Economics Association *Handbook of Food Preparation*. Additional terms appear in most of the Review Questions at the end of each unit.

Food Constituents

Proteins
Fats
Carbohydrates
  Sugars
  Starches
  Pectins
  Cellulose
Vitamins
  Fat soluble
  Water soluble
Enzymes
Water
Minerals

Reactions or Processes
(Starches and Proteins)

Hydration
Hydration capacity
Polymers
Gelation

Physical Properties

Density
Specific gravity
Surface tension
Viscosity
Heat of Fusion
Heat of Vaporization
Molal Lowering of Freezing point
Crystallization

Protein Terms and Processes

Peptization
Denaturation
Coagulation

Starch Terms and Processes

Gelatinization
Syneresis

Fat and Oil Terms and Processes

Single bond
Saturated fat
Double bond
Unsaturated fat
Polyunsaturated
Monoglyceride
Diglyceride
Triglyceride
Fat/oil
Oxidation
Oxidative rancidity
Hydrolytic rancidity
Hydrogenation
Flash point
Smoke point

Dispersion Systems

True solutions
  Solute
  Solvent
Colloids
  Dispersed phase
  Dispersion medium
  Interface
  Emulsions
  Foams
  Sol
  Gel
Suspensions

Baked Products

Browning Mechanisms
  Dextrinization
  Caramelization
  Maillard Reaction
Leavening system
Leavening agent
Leavening gas

Descriptive Terms Used in Judging Characteristics of Baked Products

Volume: The amount of a baked product produced from a specific amount of batter. Volume will be small (poor), average (good), large (excellent).

Appearance: The shape, condition of the top crust, and the color of the exterior surface (may at times include the color of interior crumb).

Shape: Symmetrical, unsymmetrical.

Condition of top crust: Level, sunken, rounded, erupted (volcano-like), pebbled, sticky, greasy, dry.

Exterior color: Pale, practically no browning, golden brown, light brown, dark brown, black (burned).

Interior color: May be affected by ingredients used, especially where egg is an ingredient.

*Texture: The size of the air cell and thickness of the cell wall constitute the "grain" of the baked product. A product is heavy, compact, or light by characteristics of cell wall and air cell.

Air cell: Small, medium, large.

Cell wall: Thin, medium, thick.

Flakiness: The layering or development of "flakes" in the crumb of certain pastries.

Mealiness: Lack of flakiness: pastry is crumbly.

Velvetiness: Smoothness of crumb as it comes between palate and the back of the tongue. Lacking velvetiness, the crumb may be harsh and rough.

Moistness: The degree of moisture within the crumb. The crumb may be wet, soggy, gummy, pleasingly moist, dry.

Tenderness: The ease with which a product may be cut, broken, or chewed. Products may vary from very tough to extremely tender. Pastries may be designated as *brittle* and *hard*.

Flavor: Should be characteristic of product. Aroma becomes part of flavor as product is eaten. A partial list of terms to describe flavor may include: sweet, bitter, soapy, nutlike, floury, flat, rancid fat, wheat-like, eggy, yeasty, bland, sour.

*Note: Many authors describe texture attributes of baked products in terms of "grain"; for example, a pound cake has a close grain.

Muffins

OBJECTIVES

*1. To give students the experience of applying principles of measurement of ingredients.
2. To acquaint students with the Muffin Method for combining ingredients for baked products.
3. To observe changes that occur in muffin batter with extended stirring of ingredients.
*4. To acquaint students with one method for evaluating quality characteristics of a food product.

PRODUCT TO BE PREPARED TO ILLUSTRATE PRINCIPLES

Muffins

PRINCIPLES

*1. Flour proteins (glutenin and gliadin) plus milk (water) plus work result in the formation of gluten.
*2. Quality of the gluten structure formed determines the quality of the baked product.
3. Stretching of gluten strands in transferring batter from mixing bowl to baking pan affects texture of the baked muffin.
4. Leavening action of baking powder is affected by:
   a. Addition of liquid (water).
   b. Temperature of baking.
*5. Coagulation of certain proteins to retain structure:
   a. Gluten.
   b. Egg (if present).
*6. Mechanisms of browning:
   a. Caramelization of sugar.
   b. Dextrinization of starch.
   c. Protein–carbohydrate interaction (Maillard Reaction).

*These objectives and principles are inherent in all baked products.

Muffins (See page 250 for Microwave Method)

Flour, all purpose	1 cup	250 ml
Baking powder	2 teaspoons	10 ml
Salt	1/2 teaspoon	2 ml
Sugar	3 tablespoons	45 ml
Milk	1/2 cup	125 ml
Egg, blended	2 tablespoons	30 ml
Vegetable oil	2 tablespoons	30 ml

1. Preheat oven to 425°F (220°C).
2. Lightly grease the *bottoms* (*not* the sides) of set of 6 muffin cups. Use additional oil.
3. Sift flour before measuring.
4. Sift together flour, baking powder, salt, and sugar in a 2-quart (2-L) bowl.
5. Blend together the milk, egg, and liquid shortening with the egg beater in a 1-quart (1-L) bowl. Do *not* beat until foamy, but oil should be broken up into fairly small globules.
6. Make a depression or "well" in the dry ingredients with a tablespoon. Add the liquid ingredients immediately.
7. Stir 5 or 6 strokes with a metal tablespoon. Some of the dry ingredients will not be wetted at this stage of blending. Remove enough batter for one muffin. (Muffin cups should be approximately 2/3 full.)
8. Stir remaining batter an additional 5 or 10 strokes or just enough until all dry ingredients are wetted. The batter should appear lumpy at this stage. Remove enough batter for four muffins. (These muffins should be typical high quality muffins when baked.
9. Stir the remaining batter an additional 50 strokes. At this stage the batter should be extremely smooth. (Be sure to note changes in the consistency of the batter during the stirring periods.) Remove enough batter for one muffin.
10. Bake in 425°F (220°C) oven for 15–20 minutes. The typical or standard muffins should be a golden brown at the end of the baking period.
11. Record total working time:_____ minutes.

CHARACTERISTICS OF HIGH QUALITY MUFFINS

Appearance: Top crust has a cauliflower-like appearance; is rather rough or pebbled; is golden brown.
Texture: Uniform distribution of gas holes; gas holes may be fairly large; the cell walls are of medium thickness.
Tenderness: Very little resistance when being bitten and chewed.
Flavor: Usually bland or very slightly sweet.
Eating Quality: Overall satisfaction in serving and eating this product is high.

EVALUATION OF PRODUCTS

Name: _____

Date: _____

Score System

Points	Quality
7	Excellent
6	Very good
5	Good
4	Medium
3	Fair
2	Poor
1	Very poor

Directions:
1. Place the numerical score in the box in the upper left hand corner.
2. Comments should justify the numerical score. Comments must be brief.
3. Evaluation of the food products must be on an *individual* basis.

Products

Quality Characteristic					
Appearance					
Consistency or Texture					
Tenderness					
Flavor					
Overall Eating Quality					

SUMMARY OUTLINE: **MUFFINS**

(Product)

Name: _____

Date: _____

Summary Outlines emphasize application of principles to basic steps in preparation of a food product. Principles may have been discussed in lecture, in laboratory, or may have been in assigned readings. Include cooking or baking temperature and know *why* a low, medium, or high temperature is used. Summaries are excellent means for review.

List of Ingredients:

Flour, all-purpose	1 cup	250 ml
Baking powder	2 teaspoons	10 ml
Salt	1/2 teaspoon	2 ml
Sugar	3 tablespoons	45 ml
Milk	1/2 cup	125 ml
Egg, blended	2 tablespoons	30 ml
Vegetable oil	2 tablespoons	30 ml

Steps in Preparation	*Principles Applied*
1. Preheat oven to 425°F (220°C).	1. Have oven ready for immediate heating of batter.
2. Lightly grease bottoms of muffin pans.	2. So batter can be transferred rapidly with least loss of carbon dioxide.
3. Sift together all dry ingredients.	3. For more even distribution, especially of baking powder (leavening agent).
4. With rotary beater blend together milk, egg, and vegetable oil.	4. a. For more even distribution of liquid ingredients; egg must be thoroughly blended with milk; oil must be broken into small globules. b. For easier blending of liquid and dry ingredients.
5. Add liquid ingredients to dry ingredients. Stir approximately 15–20 strokes. Stir only until mixture appears lumpy and dry ingredients are wetted.	5. a. To hydrate flour. b. To dissolve sugar and salt. c. To initiate leavening reaction. d. To regulate gluten development.
6. Carefully spoon batter into pans.	6. a. To prevent stretching of gluten. b. To prevent loss of leavening gas. c. To avoid trapping air which forms pockets and gives poor texture.

7. Bake at 425°F (220°C) for 15–20 minutes.	7. a. High temperature necessary for rapid production of carbon dioxide.
	b. Coagulate proteins for structure.
	c. Gelatinize starch for structure.
	d. Browning reactions include:
	  (1) Caramelization of sucrose and lactose (sugars).
	  (2) Dextrinization of starch.
	  (3) Maillard reaction.

Note: A Summary Outline sheet is placed at the end of each lesson in the baked products unit.

Additional sheets are found in Appendix B.

REVIEW QUESTIONS

1. What leavening system is used in muffins?
2. What is the effect of dropping the batter from a distance into the muffin pan?
3. What is the effect of overmanipulation of the batter on the quality of the finished muffin?
4. Why is there less danger of overmixing muffins if:
   a. They are made with a higher proportion of sugar to flour?
   b. Cornmeal or whole wheat flour is substituted for a part of the all-purpose flour?
5. List the characteristics of a high quality muffin.
6. List several possible defects which might be found in muffins and indicate the cause(s) of each defect.

GENERAL REVIEW QUESTIONS ON BAKED PRODUCTS

Note: Some of these questions cannot be answered by the student at this early stage in his study of the principles of food preparation. However, these questions placed at this point should serve as a guide to some of the important principles that are to be covered. Specific review questions on each of the baked products follow the lesson on that product.

1. Give the essential steps in each of the following methods of combining ingredients:
   a. Muffin Method.
   b. Biscuit Method.
   c. Pastry Method.
   d. Cake, Conventional Method.
   e. Cake, Quick Mix Method.
   f. Foam-type Cake Methods.
   g. Cream Puff Method.
2. a. How are the proteins of wheat (glutenin and gliadin) transformed to gluten?
   b. What effect does heat have on the gluten structure?
3. List the function(s) of each of the following ingredients in baked products:
   a. Flour.
   b. Sugar.
   c. Baking powder.
   d. Salt.
   e. Egg.
   f. Water.
   g. Milk.
4. a. What are the three gases which produce leavening action?
   b. Briefly describe how each gas may be produced.
5. a. How are single-action and double-action baking powder similar?
   b. How are they different?
   c. What are the advantages of each type of baking powder?
   d. What are the disadvantages?
6. Tell how each of the following will effect the formation and/or the resulting characteristics of the gluten structure:
   a. Type of flour.
   b. Amount of flour.
   c. Sugar.
   d. Baking powder residue.
   e. Salt.
   f. Egg.
   g. An increase or decrease of milk or water.
   h. Fat.

7. a. In preparing certain baked products the oven must be preheated and the pan prepared before measuring the ingredients. Why?
   b. List the products where this is required.
8. Summarize the reactions that take place as any baked product is heated in the oven. Give some indication as to when in the baking process each reaction takes place (this could be done as a sort of a time line). Be sure to account for each of the following constituents or reactions: leavening agents, fats, sugars, salts, protein, starch, water, and browning reactions (Maillard Reaction, caramelization, and dextrinization).

212°F 100°C   Boiling point of water

70°C   Coagulation temperature of egg protein

32°F 0°C   Freezing point of water

9. Each baked product has an optimum oven temperature for obtaining the highest quality finished product. For each of the products listed below, state the optimum oven temperature and tell briefly why it is the optimum temperature for that product.

Muffins

    Temperature: _____

    Reason(s)

Cream puffs

    Temperature: _____

    Reason(s)

Baking powder biscuits

    Temperature: _____

    Reason(s)

Yeast leavened products

    Temperature: _____

    Reason(s)

Butter type cakes

    Temperature: _____

    Reason(s)

Pie pastry

    Temperature: _____

    Reason(s)

Foam type cakes

    Temperature: _____

    Reason(s)

Baking Powder Biscuits

OBJECTIVES

1. To acquaint the student with the Biscuit Method for combining ingredients for baked products.
2. To observe the effect of kneading on the biscuit dough.
3. To observe changes that occur in a baking powder biscuit as a result of kneading.
4. To demonstrate the effect of buttermilk (acid)-soda leavening system on selected quality characteristics.
5. To explain the format for applying principles of preparation to the product.

PRODUCT TO BE PREPARED TO ILLUSTRATE PRINCIPLES

Baking powder biscuits
Buttermilk biscuits

PRINCIPLES

1. Flakiness is dependent on:
   a. Type of fat used.
   b. The kneading process.
2. After carbon dioxide has been released by leavening reaction, residues from the system remain in the baked product and may effect flavor.
3. Principles 1, 2, 4, 5, and 6 given in the lesson on muffins also apply to baking powder biscuits.

Baking Powder Biscuits (Kneaded)

Flour, all-purpose	1 1/2 cups	375 ml
Baking powder	2 teaspoons	10 ml
Salt	1/2 teaspoon	2 ml
Shortening	1/4 cup	50 ml
Milk	1/2 cup + 1 tablespoon	140 ml

1. Preheat oven to 425°F (220°C).
2. Lightly grease a 2-inch (5 cm) diameter portion of the baking sheet for the Drop Biscuit (Step 6).
3. Sift together all dry ingredients.
4. Cut shortening into dry ingredients until the shortening has been cut into pieces the size of small grains of rice. (Use pastry blender.)
5. Add the milk all in one portion. Stir with a metal tablespoon for approximately 10 strokes.
6. Cut out enough dough for one "drop" biscuit. Place the dough on greased portion of baking sheet. See the note following Characteristics of High Quality Drop Biscuits.
7. Use approximately 1 tablespoon (15 ml) more flour to *lightly* flour the breadboard.
8. Turn remaining dough out onto the lightly floured board. Dip fingertips into small amount of flour; pat out dough to 1-inch (2.5 cm) thickness; fold half of the dough onto the other half; if necessary, lightly flour portion of board from which dough has been removed.
9. Again pat dough 1-inch (2.5 cm) thick; repeat manipulation processes in Step 8 until the dough has been patted out and folded at least 5 or 6 times (total).
10. After the last folding of the dough, roll the dough 3/4 inch (2 cm) thick with a lightly floured rolling pin.
11. Dip biscuit cutter into flour before cutting each biscuit. Use even pressure in cutting down on the dough to get more evenly shaped biscuits.
12. Place the cut biscuits on an ungreased baking sheet. Have sides of biscuits touching if soft biscuits are desired. Set biscuits apart for crisp crusted biscuits. These should be *typical, control,* or *standard kneaded* biscuits.
13. Knead the scraps of dough together until the dough becomes very elastic (about 50 kneading strokes). Roll dough 3/4 inch (2 cm) thick. Cut several biscuits of these "re-rolls". Place on ungreased baking sheets with biscuits cut at Step 12.
14. Place in an oven preheated to 425°F (220°C). Bake for approximately 15 minutes. Typical biscuits will be golden brown.
15. Record total working time:_____minutes.

Buttermilk Biscuits (Kneaded)

Flour, all-purpose	1 1/2 cups	375 ml
Baking powder	1 teaspoon	5 ml
Soda	1/2 teaspoon	2 ml
Salt	1/2 teaspoon	2 ml
Shortening	1/4 cup	50 ml
Buttermilk	2/3 cup	150 ml

1. Follow directions as given for Baking Powder Biscuits (Kneaded).

CHARACTERISTICS OF HIGH QUALITY BAKING POWDER BISCUITS

Appearance: Top crust is a pale, golden brown; top crust is slightly rough; sides are straight.
Texture: Uniform small gas holes; relatively thin cell walls; crumb will peel off in "sheets" or layers.
Tenderness: Outer crust is crisp, yet tender; little resistance when bitten into. Interior is tender with little resistance when bitten.
Flavor: Very bland, mild; flavor of table fat or jelly will predominate.

CHARACTERISTICS OF HIGH QUALITY DROP BISCUITS

Appearance:
  Exterior: Top crust is pale, golden brown; top crust is slightly rough.
  Interior: Crumb color will be white.
Texture: Gas holes larger and less uniform than in kneaded; cell walls slightly thicker.
Tenderness: Outer crust should be very crisp, yet tender; interior very tender, little resistance to bite.
Flavor: Very bland, mild; flavor of table fat or jelly will predominate.

Note: In order to make drop biscuits of optimum quality the dough must be more moist than for kneaded biscuits. The recipe for kneaded biscuits may be used for drop biscuits by increasing the milk to 1 cup (250 ml).

CHARACTERISTICS OF HIGH QUALITY BUTTERMILK BISCUITS

Appearance:
  Exterior: Top crust is golden brown; may be slightly rough; sides are straight.
  Interior: Crumb color will be creamy white.
Texture: Gas holes vary in size from small to medium large. Cell walls may vary from slightly thick to relatively thin. Crumb will "peel off" in small sheets or layers.
Tenderness: Outer crust is crisp, yet tender; very little resistance when bitten into. Interior is extremely tender. Practically no resistance when bitten.
Flavor: Bland, mild flavor with a slightly acid aftertaste.

REVIEW QUESTIONS

1. *Flakiness* in biscuits.
   a. What is the role of each of the ingredients:
      (1) Fat?
      (2) Flour?
   b. What type of fat must be used?
   c. At what steps in the procedure is *flakiness* developed?
2. Describe how each of the following treatments would affect the quality of the finished biscuit. Why is this effect produced?
   a. Overkneading the dough.
   b. Too much liquid.
   c. Biscuit cut over the edge of the dough.
   d. Tops brushed with milk.
3. Why is an oven temperature of 425°F (220°C) used for baking biscuits?
4. Distinguish between *flakiness* and *tenderness*. What different factors influence each of these quality characteristics?
5. List the characteristics of a high quality kneaded biscuit.
6. List the characteristics of a high quality buttermilk biscuits.
7. a. How is carbon dioxide produced in the buttermilk-soda system?
   b. How does this differ from the leavening system in a baking powder biscuit?
8. Why is a buttermilk biscuit more tender than a baking powder biscuit?

EVALUATION OF PRODUCTS

Name: _____

Date: _____

Score System

Points	Quality
7	Excellent
6	Very good
5	Good
4	Medium
3	Fair
2	Poor
1	Very poor

Directions:

1. Place the numerical score in the box in the upper left hand corner.
2. Comments should justify the numerical score. Comments must be brief.
3. Evaluation of the food products must be on an *individual* basis.

Products

Quality Characteristic					
Appearance					
Consistency or Texture					
Tenderness					
Flavor					
Overall Eating Quality					

SUMMARY OUTLINE: _____   _Name:_ _____
                              (Product)   _Date:_ _____

Summary Outlines emphasize application of principles to basic steps in preparation of a food product. Principles may have been discussed in lecture, in laboratory, or may have been in assigned readings. Include cooking or baking temperature and know _why_ a low, medium, or high temperature is used. Summaries are excellent means for review.

List of Ingredients:

Steps in Preparation	Principles Applied
1.	1.

Yeast Breads

OBJECTIVES

1. To give students the opportunity to prepare a product leavened by yeast.
2. To acquaint students with selected factors that will affect quality characteristics of yeast dough:
   a. Temperature for yeast activity.
   b. Effect of salt on yeast activity.
   c. Effect of kneading.
3. To give students the opportunity to use dried milk solids in a baked product.
4. To develop an extremely elastic gluten structure in the dough.

PRODUCT TO BE PREPARED TO ILLUSTRATE PRINCIPLES

Yeast rolls

PRINCIPLES

1. Dry yeast is blended with warm water and sugar; this yeast mixture is then held at a warm temperature. This procedure will:
   a. Hydrate dry yeast cells.
   b. Provide sugar for growth of yeast cells thereby producing carbon dioxide for leavening.
   c. Provide a warm temperature for more rapid growth of yeast cells. Cold temperature delays yeast growth; too high a temperature kills yeast cells.
   d. Avoid depressing effect of salt on rate of yeast growth.
2. Kneading of dough develops extremely elastic gluten structure essential for proper fermentation.
3. Kneading of dough more evenly distributes yeast cells throughout the dough structure for more even leavening action.
4. Kneading dough after first fermentation period further increases dispersion of yeast and gas cells.
5. Oven heat causes rapid increase in yeast activity with increase in loaf volume during first part of the baking period.
6. Factors which contribute to the browning of the crust:
   a. Dextrinization of starch.
   b. Caramelization of sugars (glucose, lactose, and sucrose).
   c. Maillard Reaction—interaction of carbohydrate and protein.

Yeast Rolls

Water, warm	1/2 cup	125 ml
Sugar	1 tablespoon	15 ml
†Dried milk solids	2 tablespoons	30 ml
*Yeast, dried	1 package	1 package
**Flour, all-purpose	2 cups	500 ml
Salt	1/2 teaspoon	2 ml
Shortening (at room temp.)	2 tablespoons	30 ml
Egg	1	1

1. Preheat oven to 400°F (200°C).
2. Measure the sugar and the dried milk solids.
***3. Measure the water and place in a 2-quart (2 L) bowl. Add the dried yeast. Stir until blended. Add the sugar and the dried milk solids. Stir until blended. Allow this yeast mixture to stand while measuring the remaining ingredients. The yeast activity is initiated.
4. Measure remaining ingredients.
***5. Add the egg and 1 cup (250 ml) of the flour to the yeast mixture. Beat until the batter is smooth. (About 100 strokes.)
***6. Add the salt, shortening, and half of the remaining flour. Stir until the mixture is smooth and well blended. If the dough is sticky at this stage, add about half of the remaining flour; stir until well blended.
7. If the dough is still too sticky to turn out on a lightly floured board, add the remaining portion of flour and stir into dough. If the dough is not sticky at the end of Step 6, use the flour that was not put into the dough to lightly flour the breadboard.
8. Put the dough onto the lightly floured board. Knead the dough until it is lightly blistered under the surface; the dough has a satiny sheen; the dough has become resilient—when punched lightly with the finger, the dough springs back.
9. Place the dough in a lightly greased bowl; lightly grease the surface of the dough. Allow dough to rise at least 10 minutes—to double in bulk is preferable when time permits. Use a plate or a clean, damp cloth to cover during fermentation.
10. *Lightly* knead the dough to evenly distribute gas cells.
***11. Shape dough into rolls; place rolls in a well-greased baking pan. Dough will make 12 pan rolls. Cut dough into 12 equal portions; round surface of the dough against the palm of the hand, or on the breadboard (not floured for this). A *thin* film of shortening on the surface of the rolls will keep them from drying during the proofing period.
12. Allow the shaped rolls to rise until double in bulk. This may take 20 minutes or longer; do not have rolls in too warm a place for this second rising period.
13. Bake rolls in an oven preheated to 400°F (200°C) for 20-25 minutes. (Rolls baked individually as in muffin pans will bake more quickly than rolls placed touching each other in a layer cake pan.)
14. Record total working time:_____minutes.

†, *, **, *** Special information is given on the following page.

Special Notes: ingredients and method of combining yeast rolls.

† *Milk:*
(a). The processing procedure to make dry milk solids requires heating the milk to a temperature at which enzymes in milk are inactivated and bacteria are destroyed. Consequently the reconstituted dried milk solids do not need to be heated and cooled in preparing yeast leavened products.
(b). One-half cup (125 ml) fresh, fluid milk can be substituted for the water + dried milk solids. Heat milk to lukewarm: add yeast and sugar. Stir to thoroughly blend. Continue at Step 4, page 38.

* *Yeast:*
Two times the normal amount of yeast has been used because of the limited amount of time for fermentation of the dough.

** *Flour:*
All-purpose flour is used so the rolls can be completed within a 2 hour laboratory period. Other types of flour (alone or in combinations) usually require a longer rising time and the rolls may not be completed within the limited time period.

*** *Combining ingredients—Shaping of dough:*
(a). The straight dough method of combining ingredients has been modified to provide more rapid yeast growth by delaying the addition of those ingredients (fat and salt) that inhibit the growth of yeast.
(b). The dough is shaped and baked as pan rolls because less time is needed; however, the dough may be formed into a loaf, which may require a longer rising and baking period.

CHARACTERISTICS OF HIGH QUALITY YEAST ROLLS

Appearance: Surface of each roll is smooth; top crust is golden brown.
Texture: Gas holes are evenly distributed; gas holes should be fairly small and uniform in size; cell walls are fairly thin.
Tenderness: Some, but very little resistance when bitten into and chewed.
Flavor: Fairly bland (may be slightly yeasty if roll is warm when tasted).

REVIEW QUESTIONS

1. a. Why are the yeast, water, sugar, and milk powder mixed together?
    b. Why is warm water used?
    c. Why is the mixture allowed to stand for 15–20 minutes?
    d. Does the flour furnish any food for the growth of the yeast? How?
    e. Why are salt and fat added so late in the mixing procedure?
2. a. Why is an extremely elastic gluten structure desirable in bread and rolls?
    b. What steps are taken to achieve this elastic structure?
3. What is the primary purpose of the second kneading operation?
4. a. Why is the surface of the rolls covered with fat during the proofing period?
    b. What other technique is also used that accomplishes the same purpose?
5. What is meant by each of the following terms?
    a. Oven spring.
    b. Dextrinization.
    c. Caramelization.
6. Describe the characteristics of a high quality yeast roll.

EVALUATION OF PRODUCTS

Name: _____

Date: _____

Score System

Points	Quality
7	Excellent
6	Very good
5	Good
4	Medium
3	Fair
2	Poor
1	Very poor

Directions:

1. Place the numerical score in the box in the upper left hand corner.
2. Comments should justify the numerical score. Comments must be brief.
3. Evaluation of the food products must be on an *individual* basis.

Products

Quality Characteristic					
Appearance					
Consistency or Texture					
Tenderness					
Flavor					
Overall Eating Quality					

SUMMARY OUTLINE:_____ *Name:* _____
(Product)

Date: _____

Summary Outlines emphasize application of principles to basic steps in preparation of a food product. Principles may have been discussed in lecture, in laboratory, or may have been in assigned readings. Include cooking or baking temperature and know *why* a low, medium, or high temperature is used. Summaries are excellent means for review.

List of Ingredients:

Steps in Preparation	Principles Applied
1.	1.

Butter Type Cakes

OBJECTIVES

1. To acquaint students with two frequently used methods for combining cake ingredients:
   a. Conventional Method.
   b. Quick Mix Method.
2. To provide an opportunity to compare quality characteristics of cakes baked by these two methods.
3. To have students recognize the importance of the relationship between proportion of ingredients and the type and amount of manipulation required to produce a typical cake by either method for combining cake ingredients.
4. To prepare a cake utilizing a food acid-baking soda leavening system.

PRODUCTS TO BE PREPARED TO ILLUSTRATE PRINCIPLES

Conventional Method Cake
Quick Mix Method Cake
Devil's Food Cake

PRINCIPLES

1. Cake flour contains the smallest amount of protein of any of the wheat flours.
2. Cake flour protein produces a weak gluten structure.
3. Plastic fat can entrap air incorporated with addition of sugar to the fat during the creaming process. The amount of air incorporated is dependent on the:
   a. Rate at which sugar is added to the fat.
   b. Amount of work done in "creaming" the fat and sugar after each addition of sugar.
4. Gluten formation is delayed or inhibited by:
   a. Sugar.
   b. Fat.
   c. High ratio of liquid to flour.
   d. Baking powder residues.
5. Gluten formation is fostered by:
   a. Low ratio of liquid to flour.
   b. Stirring or beating.
6. Gluten structure is augmented by egg protein.
7. Sulphate-phosphate baking powder requires heat for full carbon dioxide production.

8. Emulsifiers in shortening give greater dispersion of the fat in the batter and the baked cake.
9. Most flavors used in cakes are fat soluble.
10. Standardization of manipulation by "strokes" and not time alone makes for more standardized quality in the baked cakes.
11. Common flavors (sugar, vanilla, lemon, spice, chocolate, and so on) may mask flavor of baking powder residues.
12. Certain foods are decidedly acid and when used in conjunction with baking soda (a base) form a leavening system.
13. Low-fat margarine, whipped margarines, or whipped butter will not yield satisfactory products in these cake recipes.
14. The sugar crystals are necessary to incorporate air during creaming; therefore, noncrystalline sweeteners cannot be substituted.

Butter Type Cake—Conventional Method

Butter, margarine, or shortening	1/4 cup	50 ml
Sugar	2/3 cup	150 ml
Vanilla	1/2 teaspoon	2 ml
Egg	1	1
Flour, cake	1 cup	250 ml
Baking powder	1 teaspoon	5 ml
Salt	1/4 teaspoon	1 ml
Milk	1/3 cup	75 ml

1. Preheat oven to 350°F (175°C).
2. Cut waxed paper to fit bottom of 8- or 9-inch (20–22 cm) diameter layer cake pan.
3. Grease *only* bottom of the cake pan; insert the waxed paper; grease the waxed paper.
4. Sift together the flour, salt, and baking powder.

By Electric Mixer:
5. Place the shortening and vanilla in the bowl. Set the mixer at medium speed. Add sugar *very* gradually. Cream until the mass is light and fluffy. The mass should be soft enough to remain on the bottom of the bowl; the mass should *not* remain balled up around the mixer blades. Total creaming time may be as long as 5–7 minutes; this creaming step is *critical.*
6. Add the beaten egg in two portions. Beat for 1 minute after each addition.
7. Add approximately half the flour mixture and half the milk. Beat at medium speed for 1 minute.
8. Add the last portion of flour and liquid. Blend for 30 seconds at medium speed; beat for 3 more minutes at high speed.
9. Push all of batter at one time into the pan. Bake at 350°F (175°C) for approximately 25 minutes.
10. Cool in upright position at least 5 minutes before removing from cake pan.
11. Record total working time:_____minutes.

By Hand Mixing:
5. Place the shortening and the vanilla in a bowl. Add about 1 teaspoon of sugar. Stir the sugar thoroughly into the shortening.
6. Repeat Step 5 until all the sugar has been added. Be sure the fat-sugar mixture is beaten until light and fluffy after each addition of the sugar. (The degree of creaming at this stage determines the texture and eating quality of the baked cake.) At this stage the fat-sugar mass should be light, fluffy, and soft enough to stay on the bottom and the sides of the mixing bowl. The mixture should be stirred or beaten beyond the stage where the mass tends to cling to the mixing spoon.
7. Add approximately half the beaten egg. Blend thoroughly with the fat-sugar mixture.
8. Repeat Step 7.
9. Add about one-third of the flour mixture to the fat-sugar mixture. Stir about 75 strokes.
10. Add about half of the milk. Stir about 15 strokes.
11. Add about half of the remaining flour. Stir 75 strokes.
12. Add the last portion of milk. Stir about 15 strokes.
13. Add the last portion of flour. Stir about 150 strokes.
14. Push all of the batter at one time into pan   Bake at 350°F (175°C) approximately 25 minutes.
15. Cool in upright position at least 5 minutes before removing from cake pan.
16. Record total working time:_____minutes.

Butter Type Cake—Quick Mix Method

Flour, cake	1 cup	250 ml
Sugar	2/3 cup	150 ml
Salt	1/4 teaspoon	1 ml
Baking powder	1 1/2 teaspoons	7 ml
*Shortening	1/4 cup	50 ml
Milk	1/2 cup	125 ml
Vanilla	1/2 teaspoon	2 ml
Egg	1	1

1. Preheat oven to 350°F (175°C).
2. Cut waxed paper to fit bottom of an 8- or 9-inch (20–22 cm) diameter layer cake pan.
3. Grease *only* the bottom of the cake pan; insert the waxed paper; grease it also.
4. Sift together into a large mixing bowl the flour, sugar, salt, and baking powder.
5. Add the shortening, approximately half of the milk, and the vanilla; beat vigorously for 2 minutes. If beaten by hand, use 150 strokes per minute. Scrape batter from the sides and bottom of bowl while mixing in order to blend uniformly. Use medium speed if using an electric mixer.
6. Add unbeaten egg and the remaining portion of milk. Beat two minutes longer at 150 strokes per minute. Use medium speed if using an electric mixer.
7. Push all of batter at one time into cake pan. Bake at 350°F (175°C) for approximately 25 minutes.
8. Cool in an upright position at least 5 minutes before removing from cake pan.
9. Record total working time:_____ minutes.

*A shortening which contains mono- and/or diglyceride type emulsifiers is recommended for all cakes combined by the Quick Mix Method.

CHARACTERISTICS OF HIGH QUALITY BUTTER TYPE CAKES

Appearance: Top crust should be slightly rounded toward the center of the layer; top crust should be pale, golden brown.

Texture: Uniform distribution of small gas holes; cell walls should be quite thin.

Tenderness: Crumb should be so tender as to "melt in the mouth" when bitten; there should be practically no resistance when bitten.

Mouth Feel: Crumb should feel "velvety" or extremely smooth as it comes into contact with the palate and the back of the mouth; crumb should be slightly moist.

Flavor: Mild sweet flavor will predominate; if butter is used, butter flavor may be apparent.

Devil's Food Cake

Flour, cake	1 cup	250 ml
Sugar	3/4 cup	175 ml
Soda	3/4 teaspoon	3 ml
Salt	1/2 teaspoon	2 ml
Cocoa	1/4 cup	50 ml
*Shortening	1/4 cup	50 ml
Buttermilk	1/2 cup	125 ml
Vanilla	1/2 teaspoon	2 ml
Egg	1	1

Fat and flour for baking pan (see Step 2)

1. Preheat oven to 350°F (175°C).
2. Lightly grease bottom of 9-inch (22 cm) diameter layer cake pan. Insert waxed paper; lightly grease paper; evenly shake 1/2 teaspoon (2 ml) flour over bottom of pan. Invert the pan to remove excess flour.
3. Sift together cake flour, sugar, soda, salt and cocoa.
4. Add vanilla to buttermilk; add approximately 2/3 of buttermilk mixture and shortening to the dry ingredients.
5. Beat for 1 minute at medium speed with an electric mixer or for 150 strokes if mixed by hand. Use a rubber spatula to scrape batter from sides of bowl. Beat for 1 more minute, medium speed of mixer, or stir an additional 150 strokes by hand. Scrape batter from sides of bowl.
6. Add remaining buttermilk and the unbeaten egg. Beat for 3 more minutes, medium speed of the mixer, or stir an additional 450 strokes.
7. Use rubber spatula to push all batter to side of bowl; then push batter into baking pan in as large masses as possible. *Note:* texture of baked cake can be impaired by way in which batter is transferred to baking pan.
8. Bake in 350°F (175°C) oven for 30–35 minutes.
9. Cool in an upright position at least 10 minutes before removing from cake pan. This is an extremely tender cake so special care must be used to remove cake from pan.
10. Record total working time:_____minutes.

*A shortening which contains mono- and/or diglyceride type emulsifiers is recommended for all cakes combined by the Quick Mix Method.

CHARACTERISTICS OF HIGH QUALITY DEVIL'S FOOD CAKE

Appearance:
Exterior: Top crust should be slightly rounded toward the center of the layer; top crust is lightly browned, but mahogany red color predominates.
Interior: Crumb color is mahogany red.
Texture: Uniform distribution of very small gas holes; cell walls should be very thin.
Tenderness: Crumb is extremely tender with practically no resistance to bite.
Mouth Feel: Crumb is dry and may be *slightly* harsh as it comes into contact with the tongue and the roof of the mouth.
Flavor: Aroma and flavor of chocolate; *slightly* sweet.

REVIEW QUESTIONS

1. a. What are the differences between all-purpose flour and cake flour?
   b. How would the substitution of all-purpose flour for cake flour affect the texture and tenderness of a cake?
2. a. What type of fat must be used in a quick mix cake?
   b. What fats can be used successfully in conventional cakes?
3. What are the differences in proportion of ingredients between a conventional mix cake and a quick mix cake?
4. a. Describe briefly the creaming process.
   b. How can the maximum volume of air be incorporated during the creaming process?
   c. Is there a "creaming process" in the Quick Mix Method?
5. List the quality characteristics of high quality butter type cakes.
6. List the quality characteristics of a high quality devil's food cake.
7. a. Explain the leavening system used in this devil's food cake recipe.
   b. How does this leavening system influence the rate of manipulation?
8. List the factors which effect the color of a devil's food cake.
9. Why would you expect the devil's food cake to be more tender than the plain butter-type cake?

EVALUATION OF PRODUCTS

Name: _____

Date: _____

Score System

Points	Quality
7	Excellent
6	Very good
5	Good
4	Medium
3	Fair
2	Poor
1	Very poor

Directions:

1. Place the numerical score in the box in the upper left hand corner.
2. Comments should justify the numerical score. Comments must be brief.
3. Evaluation of the food products must be on an *individual* basis.

Products

Quality Characteristic					
Appearance					
Consistency or Texture					
Tenderness					
Flavor					
Overall Eating Quality					

SUMMARY OUTLINE: _____ *Name:* _____

(Product)

Date: _____

Summary Outlines emphasize application of principles to basic steps in preparation of a food product. Principles may have been discussed in lecture, in laboratory, or may have been in assigned readings. Include cooking or baking temperature and know *why* a low, medium, or high temperature is used. Summaries are excellent means for review.

List of Ingredients:

Steps in Preparation	Principles Applied
1.	1.

SUMMARY OUTLINE: _____ Name: _____
(Product)
Date: _____

Summary Outlines emphasize application of principles to basic steps in preparation of a food product. Principles may have been discussed in lecture, in laboratory, or may have been in assigned readings. Include cooking or baking temperature and know _why_ a low, medium, or high temperature is used. Summaries are excellent means for review.

List of Ingredients:

Steps in Preparation	Principles Applied
1.	1.

Cream Puffs and Popovers

OBJECTIVES

1. To illustrate leavening action as water is converted to steam in a baked product.
2. To illustrate emulsifying properties of egg protein.
3. To illustrate the extensibility of egg protein.
4. To acquaint students with unique method for combining ingredients for cream puffs.

PRODUCTS TO BE PREPARED TO ILLUSTRATE PRINCIPLES

Cream puffs
Popovers

PRINCIPLES

1. Starch plus water plus heat in correct ratios produce a gelatinized starch gel.
2. Melted fat separates the starch granules in flour.
3. Separated starch granules have the ability to absorb liquid equally when flour is added to boiling water-fat mixture.
4. Boiling temperature of water is essential for maximum gelatinization of starch.
5. Cool starch paste ($140°F$ or $60°C$) to prevent premature coagulation of egg protein.
6. Presence of fat inhibits or delays gluten formation.
7. Popovers contain no fat; therefore development of gluten structure is critical.
8. Steam formation for leavening action is dependent on initial oven temperature.

Cream Puff Shells

Water	1/4 cup	50 ml
Butter or margarine	2 tablespoons	30 ml
Salt	few grains	few grains
Flour, all-purpose	1/4 cup	50 ml
Egg, well-blended (not foamy)	1	1

1. Preheat oven to 425°F (220°C).
2. Lightly grease three areas of baking sheet, each area approximately 2 inches in diameter. Allow approximately 3 inches between greased areas.
3. Place water, butter, and salt in smallest size saucepan; heat until the butter is melted and the water boils *vigorously.*
4. Add the flour all in one portion to the vigorously boiling water-fat mixture. Stir quickly with a wooden spoon to get flour well blended with the water-fat mixture. Remove saucepan from the heat for the last part of the stirring process. As the flour becomes well blended, it tends to form a ball around the spoon. The partially cooked starch should hold the imprint of a metal spoon if the flour has been properly blended and heated sufficiently.
5. Partially cool the cooked starch paste.
6. Add half of the well-beaten egg to the starch paste; stir vigorously to blend.
7. Add the remaining half of the egg; stir vigorously to blend.
8. Clean sides of pan and mixing spoon with rubber spatula. If necessary, blend so final paste mixture is smooth throughout.
9. Divide paste mixture into approximately three equal portions. Place one portion on each of the greased areas of the baking sheet.
10. Bake in a 425°F (220°C) oven until lightly golden brown (15–20 minutes); reduce oven setting to 350°F (175°C); bake for 20 more minutes; reduce heat still further and bake until centers are fairly dry. Puffs can be pricked with a fork about 10 minutes before removing from oven in order to speed the drying.
11. Puff shells should be cold before they are filled.
12. Record total working time:_____minutes.

CHARACTERISTICS OF HIGH QUALITY CREAM PUFF SHELLS

Appearance: Top surface is irregular; top crust is golden brown.
Texture: At least one large gas hole formed in the interior of the puff.
Tenderness: Outer crust is tender.
Moistness: Outer crust is crisp; interior membranes may be *slightly* moist.
Flavor: Outer crust should be bland; if butter is used, its flavor may be apparent.

Popovers

Flour, all-purpose	1/2 cup	125 ml
Salt	1/4 teaspoon	1 ml
Milk	1/2 cup	125 ml
Egg	1	1

Vegetable oil to grease custard cups

1. Preheat oven to 425°F (220°C).
2. Thoroughly grease bottom and sides of 3 or 4 deep custard cups, cast iron popover pans, or deep aluminum muffin tins.
3. Sift salt and flour together into a 1-quart (1 L) mixing bowl.
4. Add egg to milk. Blend.
5. Add egg-milk mixture to flour mixture. Use a rotary beater to blend liquid and dry ingredients. Beat until mixture is just smooth. (To overbeat will reduce volume).
6. Fill custard cups or popover pans 1/3 to 1/2 full. Fill muffin tins 1/2 full.
7. Set custard cups in a shallow cake pan. This is for convenience in handling cups during baking. Place pan in oven.
8. Bake in a 425°F (220°C) oven until medium golden brown (40–45 minutes); oven temperature may be reduced to 350°F (175°C) for last 10 minutes of baking to prevent overbrowning.
9. Popovers customarily are served hot from the oven.
10. Record total working time:_____ minutes.

CHARACTERISTICS OF HIGH QUALITY POPOVERS

Appearance: Irregular contour; surface smooth. Top crust is golden brown.
Texture: At least 1 large gas hole formed in the interior of the popover. With formation of several medium size gas holes, several medium thick cell walls will have formed as "sheets" between gas holes.
Tenderness: Outer crust is crisp. Interior portions have slight resistance when bitten.
Moistness: Outer crust is relatively dry; interior membranes may be moist.
Flavor: Bland; possible slight egg flavor.

REVIEW QUESTIONS

1. a. Into what type of colloid system is the fat dispersed in cream puffs?
    b. List some other food products that are also examples of this system.
2. a. Why must the fat-water mixture be boiling vigorously before the flour is added?
    b. What functions do eggs serve in cream puffs? In popovers?
    c. What happens if the starch paste is too hot when the egg is added?
    d. Why are cream puffs and popovers started in a 425°F (220°C) oven?
    e. Why is the temperature reduced to 350°F (175°C)?
    f. Why are cream puffs pricked during baking?
    g. Why is the baking sheet greased only in spots?
3. Describe briefly the leavening of cream puffs and popovers.
4. List the quality characteristics of a high quality cream puff.
5. List the quality characteristics of a high quality popover.
6. How might overbeating cause reduced volume in a popover?

EVALUATION OF PRODUCTS

Name: _____

Date: _____

Score System

Points	Quality
7	Excellent
6	Very good
5	Good
4	Medium
3	Fair
2	Poor
1	Very poor

Directions:

1. Place the numerical score in the box in the upper left hand corner.
2. Comments should justify the numerical score. Comments must be brief.
3. Evaluation of the food products must be on an *individual* basis.

Products

Quality Characteristic					
Appearance					
Consistency or Texture					
Tenderness					
Flavor					
Overall Eating Quality					

SUMMARY OUTLINE: _____ _ _Name:_ _____
(Product)

Date: _____

Summary Outlines emphasize application of principles to basic steps in preparation of a food product. Principles may have been discussed in lecture, in laboratory, or may have been in assigned readings. Include cooking or baking temperature and know _why_ a low, medium, or high temperature is used. Summaries are excellent means for review.

List of Ingredients:

Steps in Preparation	Principles Applied
1.	1.

SUMMARY OUTLINE:_____ Name:_____
(Product)

Date:_____

Summary Outlines emphasize application of principles to basic steps in preparation of a food product. Principles may have been discussed in lecture, in laboratory, or may have been in assigned readings. Include cooking or baking temperature and know *why* a low, medium, or high temperature is used. Summaries are excellent means for review.

List of Ingredients:

Steps in Preparation	Principles Applied
1.	1.

Fats and Oils

OBJECTIVES

1. To make students aware of the variety of fats and oils and how the properties of each are dependent on source and processing treatment.
2. To acquaint students with quality characteristics of a selected group of fats and oils.

PRODUCTS TO BE INSPECTED TO ILLUSTRATE PRINCIPLES

Butter: stick, whipped
Margarine: stick, soft, whipped, low-fat
Lard
Cottonseed oil
Corn oil
Safflower oil
Olive oil
Hydrogenated vegetable oil: plain, butter flavored
Hydrogenated animal fat blended with hydrogenated vegetable oil

PRINCIPLES

1. Degree of plasticity of a fat at room temperature is dependent on:
   a. Length of carbon chains in the fatty acid.
   b. Number of double bonds (degree of unsaturation) in the fatty acid.
   c. Amount of air incorporated.
2. Hydrogenation process reduces the number of double bonds in a fat or oil.
3. Nutrient value can be fortified by addition of vitamins.
4. Addition of emulsifiers to shortening increases the degree of dispersion of the shortening in baked products.
5. Source of fat or oil may contribute a characteristic flavor to the product.
6. Whipped products:
   a. Plasticity depends on the amount of air incorporated.
   b. The incorporated air changes the density of the fat.
   c. Whipped fats can not be used to substitute for solid fat in the recipes in this manual.

REVIEW QUESTIONS

1. Define or describe briefly each of the following terms:
   a. Saturated fatty acid.
   b. Unsaturated fatty acid.
   c. Hydrogenation.
   d. Smoke point.
   e. Emulsion.
   f. Immiscible.
   g. Emulsifying agent.
   h. Polar molecule.
   i. Antioxidant.
   j. Synergist.
   k. Pro-oxidant.
   l. Sequestering agent
2. List several common fats and give the source of each of the fats named.
   a. With a high content of unsaturated fatty acids.
   b. With a high content of saturated fatty acids.
3. a. What are the two types of emulsions?
   b. In the table, list several foods which are examples of emulsions.

Food	Type of Emulsion	Dispersed Phase	Dispersing Medium	Emulsifier(s)
Cream puff	O/W	Butterfat	Water	Egg yolk Gelatinized starch
Butter	W/O	Water	Butterfat	Milk proteins
Milk				
Cheese				

   c. Why must considerable work be done in making an emulsion?
   d. How are emulsions stabilized?
4. a. Name several antioxidants which can legally be used in foods.
   b. Which of the antioxidants named above has the best "carry through" properties in baked goods?

CHARACTERISTICS OF FATS AND OILS

Type of Fat	Source	Consistency at 72° F (22°C)	Per Cent Fat as Purchased	Added Ingredients	Flavor

Pie Pastry: Fruit Pies

OBJECTIVES

1. To acquaint the student with the Pastry Method for combining ingredients.
2. To give the student the opportunity to study factors which affect the quality characteristics of pie pastry:
   a. Ratio of fat to flour.
   b. Type of fat used.
   c. Type of flour used.
   d. Amount of liquid used.
   e. Kind and extent of manipulation.
3. To illustrate factors that affect quality characteristics of a baked pastry shell.
4. To discuss principles related to the preparation of fruit-filled pies.

PRODUCT TO BE PREPARED TO ILLUSTRATE PRINCIPLES

Pie pastry   Apple pie—fresh fruit
                         Cherry pie—frozen fruit

PRINCIPLES

1. Pieces of plastic fat coated with flour particles are pressed into "sheets" or "layers" between strands of gluten during the rolling process.
2. During baking the fat melts into the gluten framework, thus leaving "sheets" or "flakes" of gluten structure in the baked pastry.
3. Rerolling pastry dough:
   a. Develops the strength of the gluten framework.
   b. Entraps air between layers of gluten; air will expand during the baking period.
4. Air is the primary leavening agent; steam is the secondary leavening agent.
5. Unbaked gluten is elastic and is easily stretched.
6. Gluten contracts as the coagulation temperature of the flour protein is reached.
7. Pared, light-colored fresh fruit may darken unless air is kept from the cut surface. Fruit may be covered with one of the following to exclude air:
   a. Tap water.
   b. Lemon juice.
   c. Sugar.
   d. Vitamin C (ascorbic acid).
   e. Mixture of Vitamin C and citric acid.
8. Sugar separates starch granules.
9. Separated starch granules have equal opportunity to absorb liquid as heat is applied.
10. Thickening the fruit juice by gelatinizing the starch before adding thawed fruit retains flavor in the pie.
11. Initial high temperature will cause coagulation of flour protein before fruit juice can "soak" the bottom crust.
12. Cornstarch and tapioca give more translucent pie fillings than flour.

Pie Pastry—Single-Crust Recipe

Flour, all-purpose	3/4 cup	175 ml
Salt	1/8 teaspoon	0.5 ml
Texturated lard or hydrogenated shortening	1/4 cup	50 ml
Milk (or Water)	2 to 3 tablespoons	30–45 ml

1. Preheat oven to 425°F (220°C).
2. Sift flour and salt together into small mixing bowl. Cut the lard into the flour with a pastry blender until the fat pieces are the size of small peas.
3. Sprinkle the milk, a half teaspoon at a time, over the fat-flour mixture: use a fork to lightly toss the moistened fat-flour mixture to the side of the bowl so all dry ingredients can come in contact with the milk as it is added. Use only enough milk to form a stiff dough. Avoid a wet, sticky dough.
4. When time permits, allow the dough to stand for 5–10 minutes for more even hydration of the flour. However, for class, there is not time for this hydration period.
5. Place the dough between two sheets of heavy waxed paper. Roll the dough to 1/8-inch (0.3 cm) thickness. Place the rolling pin at the center of the mound of dough and roll from the center toward the outer edges of the dough. Keep even pressure on the rolling pin so the pastry will be of uniform thickness. It may be necessary to loosen the waxed paper from the pastry during the rolling period to keep the paper smooth and to obtain pastry of even thickness. Roll the dough to a circle at least 1 inch (2.5 cm) larger than the pie pan. Pastry can be formed into two 6-inch (15 cm) or one 8-inch (20 cm) pie shells.
6. Loosen pastry dough from the waxed paper with a minimum stretching of the pastry.
7. Ease the dough into the pie pan but be careful not to stretch the dough. Gently press the pastry dough against the bottom and sides of the pie pan. Trim the crust even with the edge of the pie pan.
8. With a fork prick the bottom and sides of the crust to allow escape of steam.
9. Bake in a 425°F (220°C) oven for 8–10 minutes or until very pale, golden brown.
10. If air is trapped under the pastry, the crust will tend to "hump" during the baking period. It is well to check the pastry shell after the first 4 or 5 minutes of baking to be sure the pastry is not "humping." If the pastry is bulging up from the bottom of the pan, quickly prick the pastry before it is "set" with baking.
11. If time permits, reroll the remaining dough 5–8 times: roll 1/8-inch (0.3 cm) thick; place on baking sheet; prick; bake. Compare with pastry shell for tenderness and flakiness.
12. Record total working time:_____ minutes.

Note: For cream pie fillings see pages 134 to 135.

CHARACTERISTICS OF HIGH QUALITY PIE PASTRY

Appearance: Surface of pastry may have small "blisters" apparent; top is very pale golden brown; edges may be *slightly* darker.
Texture: Pastry should show evidences of layers or "flakes"; gas cells should be medium large.
Tenderness: The pastry should "melt in the mouth"; there should be *very* little resistance when bitten or when cut with a fork.
Flavor: Usually quite bland, but type of fat used may influence the flavor of the pastry.

Pie Pastry—Double-crust for 6-inch Fruit Pie

Flour, all-purpose	1 cup	250 ml
Salt	1/4 teaspoon	1 ml
Texturated lard or shortening	1/3 cup	75 ml
Milk	3 tablespoons	45 ml

1. Preheat oven to 425°F (220°C).
2. Sift together flour and salt into smallest size bowl. With a pastry blender, cut the fat into the flour until the fat is the size of peas, approximately 1/4-inch (0.6 cm) diameter.
3. Add milk gradually, stirring with a fork to evenly distribute the liquid. Add as little liquid as possible to hold the dough together.
4. Divide dough into two portions; use approximately two thirds of dough for the lower crust. Shape dough into rounds; place between sheets of waxed paper for rolling.
5. Roll dough not more than 1/8-inch (0.3 cm) thick. (Invert pie pan over dough to be sure dough extends 1-inch (2.5 cm) beyond the rim of the pie pan. Excess dough beyond the 1-inch (2.5 cm) perimeter can be trimmed away after the waxed paper has been removed from one side.)
6. Ease dough into pie pan being careful not to stretch the pastry. Lightly hold pastry in position at center of pie pan while arranging the pastry against the sides. Cut excess pastry away from the rim of the pie pan using a sharp knife.
7. Add pie filling.
8. *Lightly* moisten the edge of the pastry around the rim of the pie pan with water (use a moistened fingertip).
9. Roll pastry for top crust—also not more than 1/8-inch (0.3 cm) thick. Place on pie filling. Gently press against the moistened pastry of bottom crust. This aids in sealing the two crusts together.
10. Trim away excess pastry as in Step 6. Dip a 3- or 4-tined fork into flour. Gently press fork against the pastry and rim of pie pan to leave firm imprint of fork in pastry. Repeat around entire rim. This further aids in binding top and bottom crusts together.
11. Use a sharp knife to make four or five 1-inch (2.5 cm) slits in the upper crust. This allows steam to escape during the baking period.
12. Place pie in oven preheated to 425°F (220°C). If top crust appears to be getting too brown, reduce heat to 350°F (175°C) after 15–20 minutes at the higher temperature. Total time: 45 minutes.
13. Place a piece of aluminum foil on a rack placed just above the floor of the oven to catch juices if pie boils over. Wash foil under hot water at end of baking period.
14. Record total working time:_____ minutes.

FRUIT PIE FILLING RECIPES

Apple Pie (one 6-inch pie)

Apples, cooking variety	1 cup		250	ml
Sugar, depending on ripeness of apples	1–2 tablespoons		15–30	ml
Cornstarch	1/2 teaspoon		2	ml
Lemon juice, if apples are very ripe	1 teaspoon		5	ml
Cinnamon or nutmeg	1/8 teaspoon or less		0.5	ml or less

1. Wash, pare, and core apples; slice into 3/8–1/2 inch (1.0–1.3 cm) slices.
2. Add lemon juice. Lemon juice added to the apple slices reduces the tendency of the apples to brown. If the apples are quite ripe, the lemon juice improves the flavor.
3. Blend cornstarch with sugar and spice. Stir into apples (use a fork).
4. Place seasoned apples in pastry-lined pie pan.
5. Place top crust on apples.
6. Complete as indicated in the directions for Double-crust Pie Pastry.

Cherry Pie (one 6-inch pie)

Cherries, sweetened-frozen, thawed*	1 cup	250 ml
Cherry juice	1/3 cup	75 ml
Sugar	1 tablespoon	15 ml
Cornstarch	2 teaspoons	10 ml

1. Blend sugar and cornstarch in smallest size saucepan. Add cherry juice and stir until blended.
2. Bring mixture to a boil over direct heat. Stir constantly until the mixture boils and loses its chalky appearance—approximately 2 or 3 minutes.
3. Remove cooked starch paste from heat: add cherries and stir just enough to get starch paste evenly distributed around cherries.
4. Place filling in pastry-lined pie pan.
5. Place top crust on filling.
6. Complete as indicated in the directions for Double-crust Pie Pastry.

*If unsweetened frozen cherries are used, increase sugar to 1/4 cup (50 ml) and cornstarch to 1 tablespoon + 1 teaspoon (20 ml).

CHARACTERISTICS OF HIGH QUALITY FRUIT PIES

Pastry
   Appearance: Top crust is golden brown: edges may be *slightly* darker; surface may have small "blisters" apparent.
   Texture: *Slightly* moist and friable (easily broken); flaky.
   Tenderness: Pastry should "melt in the mouth."

Fillings
   Appearance: Fruit pieces should appear intact; apple slices will appear moist; cherries should appear plump.
   Body and Texture: Fruit pieces are tender and soft; juice has the consistency of a soft starch pudding.
   Flavor: Typical of fruit used; spice flavor must be mild.

REVIEW QUESTIONS

1. a. What are the similarities in the Pastry Method and Biscuit Method of combining ingredients?
   b. What are the differences?
2. How do the basic steps in the manipulative procedure effect the characteristics of the finished pastry?
3. a. Discuss flakiness and tenderness in pie crust.
   b. What causes a pie crust to be flaky and not be tender?
   c. What causes a pie crust to be tender and not be flaky?
4. What happens when too much water or milk is added to a pie dough?
5. What is the advantage of milk over water in making pie pastry?
6. Describe how each of the following treatments would affect the quality of the finished pastry.
   a. An increased amount of fat.
   b. Use of a very soft (low melting point) plastic fat.
   c. Use of cake flour rather than all-purpose flour.
7. a. Why is the bottom of a single shell pastry pricked with a fork before baking?
   b. How can a soggy bottom crust in a cherry pie be prevented?
8. Describe the characteristics of a high quality pie.

EVALUATION OF PRODUCTS

Name: _____

Date: _____

Score System

Points	Quality
7	Excellent
6	Very good
5	Good
4	Medium
3	Fair
2	Poor
1	Very poor

Directions:

1. Place the numerical score in the box in the upper left hand corner.
2. Comments should justify the numerical score. Comments must be brief.
3. Evaluation of the food products must be on an *individual* basis.

Products

Quality Characteristic					
Appearance					
Consistency or Texture					
Tenderness					
Flavor					
Overall Eating Quality					

EVALUATION OF TWO-CRUST PIES

Name: _____

Date: _____

Type of Filling: _____

Quality Characteristic	7 Excellent	6 Very Good	5 Good	4 Medium	3 Fair	2 Poor	1 Very Poor
Crust: Color and Appearance							
Crust: Texture							
Crust: Tenderness							
Filling: Appearance							
Filling: Body and Texture							
Filling: Flavor							
Overall Eating Quality							

Note: A 2-crust pie is evaluated on quality characteristics of pastry, quality characteristics of the filling and finally for its overall eating quality (pastry + filling). Place comments for a pastry to be rated "Good" in column 5.

SUMMARY OUTLINE: _____ *Name:* _____
(Product)

Date: _____

Summary Outlines emphasize application of principles to basic steps in preparation of a food product. Principles may have been discussed in lecture, in laboratory, or may have been in assigned readings. Include cooking or baking temperature and know *why* a low, medium, or high temperature is used. Summaries are excellent means for review.

List of Ingredients:

Steps in Preparation	Principles Applied
1.	1.

Deep-Fat Frying

OBJECTIVES

1. To give students an opportunity to relate properties of fats and oils to factors to be considered in deep-fat frying.
2. To acquaint students with the relationship between composition of the food product and temperature at which food is deep-fat fried.
3. To acquaint students with the factors and their interrelationships that effect the quality of deep-fat fried batter and dough products:
   a. Type of ingredients used.
   b. Proportion of ingredients used.
   c. Extent of manipulation.
4. To acquaint students with factors that influence fat absorption by deep-fat fried products.

PRODUCTS TO BE PREPARED TO ILLUSTRATE PRINCIPLES

Doughnut holes
Fruit and/or vegetable fritters

PRINCIPLES

1. Fats or oils used for the frying medium should have a high smoke point:
   a. Smoke point is lowered by the presence of low molecular weight fatty acids in the fat.
   b. Smoke point is lowered by the presence of mono- and/or diglycerides in super-glycerinated fats.
   c. Smoke point is lowered by the presence of free fatty acids in the fat:
      (1) Not all free fatty acids may have been removed during commercial processing of the fat.
      (2) Free fatty acids are liberated by breakdown of the fat during heating (cooking of food product).
   d. The smoke point of each fat is lowered as the surface area of the fat in the frying pan is increased.
   e. Smoke point is lowered by the presence of food particles that break away from the food being fried and remain in the fat during the frying period.
   f. Smoke point for a fat is lowered each time the fat is used for deep-fat frying.

2. The *rate* at which a fat breaks down is dependent on:
   a. Temperature to which fat is heated.
   b. Length of time the fat is heated during a frying period.
   c. Accumulation of food particles in the fat during the frying period.
   d. Surface area of fat exposed to air during the frying period.
3. The temperature at which a food product is fried is dependent on characteristics of that food:
   a. Raw meat or fish which is to be cooked during the frying period must be cooked slowly at a relatively low temperature.
   b. Foods which are quickly cooked as doughnuts or fritters can be cooked at higher temperatures.
4. The amount of fat absorbed by a food product during frying is dependent on:
   a. Smoke point of the fat used for the frying medium.
   b. Temperature-time relationship during the frying period.
   c. Composition of the food product being fried:
      (1) Batter and dough products are affected by:
         (a) Amount of flour.
         (b) Amount of liquid.
         (c) Amount of sugar.
         (d) Amount of fat.
         (e) Amount of manipulation related to the ingredients used and their proportion.
      (2) Fatty foods absorb more fat than less fatty foods.
   d. Surface area of the food product being fried.
5. Factors to consider in selecting a fat for deep-fat frying:
   a. Smoke point: low smoke point indicates rapid breakdown of fat with accompanying changes in flavor.
   b. Presence of mono- and/or diglyceride emulsufiers: smoke point is lower with these emulsifiers present.
   c. Since oils remain liquid at room temperature, oil absorbed during frying will remain liquid during storage of a product such as doughnuts. The surface of the stored doughnuts feels "oily."
   d. Natural flavor of the fat. Usually a bland flavor is desired so the flavor of the food will predominate.
   e. Cost of the fat or oil may become a factor.
   f. Temperature to which the fat will be heated relates to the stability of the fat during the heating period.
6. Browning of deep-fat fried products depends on:
   a. Time–temperature relationship during frying.
   b. Amount of carbohydrate in food or coating material.
   c. Type of carbohydrate in food or coating material.
   d. The degree of gluten development.

Note of caution: Temperatures used for deep fat frying, 365°–375°F (185°–190°C), are much higher than the boiling point of water. Handle hot fats with *extreme caution*!

Doughnut Holes

Flour, all-purpose	2 cups	500 ml
Baking powder	1 tablespoon	15 ml
Salt	1/2 teaspoon	2 ml
Nutmeg	1/4 teaspoon	1 ml
Cinnamon	1/4 teaspoon	1 ml
Sugar	1/2 cup	125 ml
Vegetable oil	2 tablespoons	30 ml
Milk	2/3 cup	150 ml
Egg yolks	2	2
Fat for deep fat frying	2 pounds	1 kg

1. Place fat for frying in a pan 5–6 inches (12–15 cm) deep with a diameter 6–7 inches (15–18 cm). There should be 2–3 inches (5–8 cm) of melted fat in the pan. *Do not use less than 2 inches (5 cm) or more than 3 inches (8 cm) of fat.* Hold over low heat while preparing the doughnut batter.
2. Sift together all dry ingredients into largest size bowl.
3. In smallest size bowl blend together the egg yolks, milk, and vegetable oil. Use the egg beater for blending. The oil must be *thoroughly blended* with the egg yolk and milk as the liquid mixture is added to the dry ingredients.
4. Add liquid ingredients to dry ingredients and stir 75 strokes. Scrape down sides of bowl and clean spoon with rubber spatula midway in the stirring period. Allow the batter to stand 5 minutes before frying.
5. Have the frying fat at 365°F (185°C) at the *beginning* of *each* frying period.
6. Use a teaspoon to cut a spoonful of batter for each doughnut. Keep the surface of the batter as smooth as possible during the cutting and spooning of the batter. The raw batter should not be larger than 1 inch in diameter for each doughnut hole.
7. Place the spoon containing the raw batter at the surface of the hot fat. Use the back of a second teaspoon to push the batter into the hot fat. (*Do not* use a rubber spatula.) *Keep surfaces as smooth as possible.* Do not fry more than 5 or 6 doughnut holes at one time. Remember to have fat at 365°F (185°C) for each frying.
8. Cook the doughnut holes for approximately 4 minutes. The doughnuts tend to turn over in the hot fat as the first side becomes brown. It will be necessary to turn a second time to get even browning during frying.
9. Use a slotted spoon to remove the cooked doughnut holes from the fat. Place doughnut holes on several layers of paper toweling to drain off excess fat.
10. For evaluation *do not* roll doughnut holes in sugar. Doughnut holes not used for evaluation may be rolled in sugar.
11. Record total working time: _____ minutes.

CHARACTERISTICS OF HIGH QUALITY DOUGHNUT HOLES

Appearance: *Outer crust* is evenly golden brown; surface is relatively smooth; doughnut hole is round.

Interior is white to grayish white. (Fat absorption can be noted by greasy appearance just under the crust. A high quality doughnut hole does not have/or has very little greasy crumb in the fried doughnut.)

Texture: Fairly compact structure; small gas cells; cell walls of medium thickness.

Tenderness: Tender, little resistance to bite; exterior may be slightly crisp immediately after frying.

Flavor: Mild, slightly spicy.

SPECIAL NOTES RELATIVE TO EVALUATION

1. The spices, especially the cinnamon, may cause a slightly grayish cast to the interior of the doughnut holes.
2. With the ratio of spices used in the recipe, the spice flavor will be quite mild immediately after the batter is fried; however, the spice flavor becomes more intense as the doughnut holes may be held in storage.
3. Immediately after frying the crust is fairly crisp; with storage sugar absorbs moisture from the air and/or there is time for equalization of moisture within the doughnut hole so the crust becomes soft.

Fruit or Vegetable Fritter Batter—(A Thick Batter)

Flour, all-purpose	1/2 cup	125 ml
Baking powder	1/2 teaspoon	2 ml
Salt	1/2 teaspoon	2 ml
Sugar (for fruit fritters only)	1 teaspoon	5 ml
Egg	1	1
Milk	1/4 cup	50 ml
Vegetable oil	1 teaspoon	5 ml
Pineapple, crushed	1/2 cup	125 ml
or		
Corn, whole kernel	1/2 cup	125 ml
Fat for deep fat frying	2 pounds	1 kg

1. Drain the crushed pineapple or whole kernel corn thoroughly. Press the juice from the pineapple with a spoon. The fruit or vegetable must be dry as it is added to the batter.
2. Place fat for frying in a pan 5–6 inches (12–15 cm) deep with a diameter 6–7 inches (15–18 cm). There should be between 2–3 inches (5–8 cm) of melted fat in pan. Do not use less than 2 inches (5 cm) or more than 3 inches (8 cm) of fat. Hold over low heat while preparing the fritter batter.
3. Sift together all the dry ingredients. (Use sugar *only* in batter for *fruit* fritters.)
4. Place the egg in smallest size bowl; add the milk and blend thoroughly with egg beater.
5. Add the liquid to the dry ingredients. Stir *not more* than 25 strokes to blend. Add the vegetable oil and stir *not more* than 10 strokes to blend.
6. Add either the well-drained pineapple or the corn; blend with *not more* than 4 or 5 strokes.
7. Have the frying fat heated to 375°F (190°C).
*8. Carefully spoon the fritter batter into the hot fat. Have the spoon near the surface of the fat; push the fritter batter into the fat with the back of a second spoon. (*Do not* use a rubber spatula.) *Do not* fry more than four fritters at one frying. Cook fritters until golden; turn and cook until second side is golden—approximately 2 minutes for each side. (The larger the fritter, the longer the time to cook the center of the fritter.)
9. Use a slotted spoon to remove the cooked fritters from the hot fat. Allow fat to drain away from the spoon before placing the fritter on several thicknesses of paper toweling to drain off excess fat.
10. Fritters may be kept warm by placing on a baking sheet in an oven preheated to 300°F (150°C).
11. For evaluation serve fritters *without* powdered sugar or table syrup.
12. Record total working time:_____minutes.

*A No. 20 ice cream scoop may be used for putting batter into the hot fat. Hold the scoop at the surface of the hot fat for putting batter into the fat.

CHARACTERISTICS OF HIGH QUALITY FRUIT OR VEGETABLE FRITTERS

Appearance: Deep golden brown; fairly smooth, even surface.
Texture: Medium-size gas holes fairly evenly distributed; cell walls may be fairly thick; evenly dispersed fruit or vegetable pieces.
Tenderness: Slight resistance to bite; fork cuts easily through crust of fritter.
Flavor: "Batter" portion is bland in flavor; flavor of fruit or vegetable should predominate.

REVIEW QUESTIONS

1. List the characteristics of composition that would give an ideal fat to use for deep-fat frying.

2. a. List some factors which will speed up the breakdown of the fat used in a deep-fat fryer.
   b. List some practical steps which might be taken to retard the rate of breakdown of the fat and extend its frying life in deep-fat frying.

3. Why are products such as breaded pork chops, chicken, and fish fillets fried at lower temperatures than doughnuts?

4. a. Doughnut recipe "A" uses 1 tablespoon (15 ml) vegetable oil per cup of flour whereas doughnut recipe "B" uses 1-1/2 tablespoon (25 ml) vegetable oil per cup of flour. If the same quantities of other ingredients are used in both "A" and "B," doughnuts from which recipe will absorb more fat during frying? Why?
   b. If only sugar were increased in recipe "B," which recipe would now be likely to have the greater fat absorption? Why?
   c. How would the increase in sugar in (b) affect the rate of browning of the doughnuts on frying?
   d. How can the change in browning be compensated for in frying the doughnuts?
   e. What practical consideration might limit the composition for browning in (d)?

5. Explain what might have been done to the doughnuts and fritters to account for the evaluations given in the table below:

Score System

Points	Quality
7	Excellent
6	Very good
5	Good
4	Medium
3	Fair
2	Poor
1	Very poor

EVALUATION OF PRODUCTS

Name: _____

Date: _____

Directions:
1. Place the numerical score in the box in the upper left hand corner.
2. Comments should justify the numerical score. Comments must be brief.
3. Evaluation of the food products must be on an *individual* basis.

Quality Characteristic	Doughnut A	Doughnut B	Doughnut C	Corn fritter	Pineapple fritter
Appearance	3 — Color too light	2 — Too dark	4 — Greasy	5	6
Consistency or Texture	3 — Wet in center	3 — Wet in center	3 — Greasy	4 — Gas cells too large	5 — Even, well distributed gas cells
Tenderness	5	4 — Crust too crisp	5	4 — Too soft	6
Flavor	4 — Raw dough	3 — Sweet	4 — Greasy	4 — Batter tastes like corn	6 — Pineapple
Overall Eating Quality	3	3	4	4	6

Starch

OBJECTIVES

1. To emphasize the necessity for separation of starch granules for even hydration and gelatinization.
2. To illustrate methods for separation of starch granules before gelatinization of the starch.
3. To illustrate effect of source of starch on thickening properties and translucency of starch gels.
4. To illustrate effect of commercial processing of starch on gel characteristics.
5. To study quality characteristics or selected starch thickened food products.
6. To demonstrate that starchs thickened products increase in viscosity as the starch paste cools.
7. To illustrate acceptable methods for the preparation of white sauce.
8. To show the relative degrees of consistency of white sauces prepared with varying ratios of flour to milk and to discuss the use of these sauces in food preparation.

PRODUCTS TO BE PREPARED TO ILLUSTRATE PRINCIPLES

Chocolate pudding
Selected commercial starch puddings
White sauce—thin, medium, thick, very thick
Selected starch gels

PRINCIPLES

1. Starch granules in the dry form tend to pack together.
2. Starch granules can be separated by:
   a. Melted fat.
   b. Other dry ingredients as sugar.
   c. Cold liquid.
3. Separated starch granules have more equal opportunity for absorbing liquid during the cooking period.
4. Starch granules will settle to bottom of the pan during cooking unless the starch mixture is stirred enough to keep the starch granules evenly dispersed throughout the mixture.
5. Gelatinization is dependent on:
   a. Ratio of liquid to starch (concentration of starch).
   b. Temperature to which the starch mixture is cooked.

6. Heat must be applied before the dry starch granule can begin to absorb liquid.
7. The source (type) of the starch will determine:
   a. The temperature required for gelatinization.
   b. The degree of thickening (consistency).
   c. Stability of starch paste on thawing after freezing.
8. Gelatinized starch granule loses its thickening property as a result of:
   a. Hydrolysis by acid.
   b. Rupturing of granule by mechanical means (overstirring).

COMPARISON OF QUALITY CHARACTERISTICS OF SELECTED STARCHES

U.S.A. Measurements

| Ingredient | Variable Number | | | | | | |
	1	2	3	4	5	6	7
*Water	7/8 cup	7/8 cup	7/8 cup	7/8 cup	3/4 cup		7/8 cup
*Lemon juice					2 T.		
*Milk						7/8 cup	
Cornstarch	1 T.			1 T.	1 T.	1 T.	
Flour		2 T.					
Tapioca			1½ T.				
Sugar				3 T.			
Flour, browned							1/4 cup

*This quantity of liquid is used to give a gel structure within a 2-hour laboratory period.

Metric Measurements

| Ingredient | Variable Number | | | | | | |
	1	2	3	4	5	6	7
*Water	200 ml	200 ml	200 ml	200 ml	170 ml		200 ml
*Lemon juice					30 ml		
*Milk						200 ml	
Cornstarch	15 ml			15 ml	15 ml	15 ml	
Flour		30 ml					
Tapioca			25 ml				
Sugar				45 ml			
Flour, browned							50 ml

*This quantity of liquid is used to give a gel structure within a 2-hour laboratory period.

A more typical gel strucutre is evident if the gels can stand for 3–4 hours before testing. The changes in gel structure due to treatment are still evident up to 24 hours after preparation.

1. For each variable, combine the starch with the cold liquid. Stir until the starch granules are separated and the mixture is homogeneous.
2. Allow variable 3 to stand for 15 minutes before cooking.
3. For each of the remaining variables, place the saucepan containing the starch mixture over direct heat. With continuous stirring, bring to a boil and boil for 1 minute. Pour into a glass custard cup.
4. For variable 3, after the 15-minute soaking period, place the saucepan over the direct heat. With continuous stirring, bring to a boil and remove *immediately* from the heat. Pour into a glass custard cup. After 5 minutes, stir mixture gently with a fork so tapioca completes gelatinization evenly.
*5. Allow all gel samples to come to room temperature before comparing.
6. For variable 7 put flour in saucepan; place pan over direct heat; stir constantly until flour is dark brown. Cool, add cold water, and cook as indicated in 3.

*Note: Evaluation sheet is on page 95.

EFFECT OF WATER TEMPERATURE ON STARCH DISPERSION

(Demonstrated by the instructor)

Cold Water
1. Stir 1 tablespoon (15 ml) of cornstarch into a glass of cold water.
   Record observations:

2. Allow glass to stand, undisturbed, for 10 minutes.
   Record observations:

Boiling Water
1. Bring 1 cup (250 ml) of water to a boil in a 1-quart (1 L) saucepan.
   Add 1 tablespoon (15 ml) of cornstarch or flour to the boiling water. Stir vigorously.
   Record observations:

CHARACTERISTICS OF HIGH QUALITY WHITE SAUCES

Appearance: White to creamy (dependent on type and amount of fat used); opaque.
Consistency: Smooth; even starch distribution and gelatinization.
  Thin: Like "thin cream"; flows freely.
  Medium: Fluid, but thick; flows slowly; like "whipping cream" before whipping.
  Thick: Thick; holds imprint of spoon or slightly "mounds" on stirring.
  Very thick: Will not flow; holds cut edge, even while warm.
Flavor: Very bland, mild; fat used may affect the flavor.

CHARACTERISTICS OF HIGH QUALITY CHOCOLATE PUDDINGS

Appearance: Moist and shiny. Film will form on top of a cooked pudding as it cools.
Consistency: Pudding should "mound" slightly. However, the pudding may be firm enough to form a mold.
Flavor: Distinct chocolate; slightly sweet, well-rounded flavor; not bitter.

WHITE SAUCE—U.S.A. MEASUREMENTS

Type	Milk	Flour	Fat	Salt	Uses
Thin	1 cup	1 tablespoon	1 tablespoon	1/4 teaspoon	soups
Medium	1 cup	2 tablespoons	2 tablespoons	1/4 teaspoon	sauces; gravies
Thick	1 cup	3 tablespoons	3 tablespoons	1/2 teaspoon	souffles
Very thick	1 cup	4 tablespoons	4 tablespoons	1/2 teaspoon	croquettes

WHITE SAUCE—METRIC MEASUREMENTS

Type	Milk	Flour	Fat	Salt	Uses
Thin	250 ml	15 ml	15 ml	1 ml	soups
Medium	250 ml	30 ml	30 ml	1 ml	sauces; gravies
Thick	250 ml	45 ml	45 ml	2 ml	souffles
Very thick	250 ml	60 ml	60 ml	2 ml	croquettes

METHODS OF PREPARATION (See page 250 for Microwave Method)

Method I. Saucepan or Frying Pan
1. Melt fat in saucepan or heavy frying pan.
2. Add flour and salt: blend until smooth.
3. Remove from heat.
4. Add milk in small portions and blend thoroughly after each addition until all milk has been added.
5. Place over direct heat: stir constantly: bring to a boil and boil for 1 minute.
6. Record total working time: _____ minutes.

Method II. Double Boiler
1. Melt fat in the upper part of the double boiler. Have the upper section of the double boiler over hot water.
2. Add flour and salt: blend until smooth.
3. Add milk gradually: stir thoroughly after each addition of milk.
4. Continue heating with occasional stirring until the mixture has thickened. Heat an additional 5 minutes after the sauce has thickened to ensure gelatinization of the starch.
5. Record total working time: _____ minutes.

Method III. Can Be Used Where a Low-Fat Product Is Desired.
1. Blend the flour and salt with 1/4 cup (50 ml) cold milk. Stir until all lumps of flour have been separated.
2. Add the remaining milk. Stir thoroughly.
3. Place the mixture in a saucepan over direct heat: stir constantly until the mixture boils: boils for 1 minute.
*4. As the mixture boils, add approximately half the indicated amount of fat for type of sauce being prepared: stir thoroughly until the fat is blended into the sauce.
5. Record total working time: _____ minutes.

*Fat may be omitted entirely if desired. This method is not recommended when the full amount of fat is to be used: it is extremely difficult to emulsify the full amount of fat.

Chocolate Pudding (See page 251 for Microwave Method.)

*Chocolate	1/2 square	1/2 square
Milk	1 cup	250 ml
Sugar	3 tablespoons	45 ml
Cornstarch	1 tablespoon	15 ml
Salt	few grains	few grains
Vanilla	1/4 teaspoon	1 ml

1. Cut the chocolate into several pieces. Place the chocolate and 3/4 cup (175 ml) milk in the upper part of the double boiler. Heat over hot water until the chocolate melts and blends with the milk. Cover during first part of heating to avoid excess loss of moisture.
2. Mix sugar, cornstarch, salt, and remaining cold milk together until smooth.
3. Add the starch mixture to the scalded milk-chocolate mixture while stirring continuously.
4. Place the upper part of the double boiler over the direct heat. While stirring continuously bring the mixture to a boil and boil 1 minute. Remove from heat.
5. Add vanilla. Pour into two dessert dishes.
6. Record total working time:_____ minutes.

*Two tablespoons (30 ml) cocoa may be substituted for the chocolate:
1. Scald 3/4 cup (175 ml) milk in upper part of double boiler.
2. Mix together cocoa, cornstarch, sugar, salt and remaining cold milk. Add this mixture to the scalded milk.
3. Continue at Step No. 4 above.

Pregelatinized Starch Pudding

Instant chocolate pudding mix	1 package	1 package
Milk	2 cups	500 ml

1. Combine ingredients according to directions on package.
2. Allow pudding to stand at least 30 minutes before evaluating.

High Amylopectin Starch Pudding

Canned chocolate pudding	1 can

1. Open can; transfer pudding to a serving dish for evaluation.
2. Optional—chill can of pudding before evaluating.

COMPARISON OF QUALITY CHARACTERISTICS OF SELECTED STARCH GELS

Variable Number	Treatment	*Appearance	Consistency and Texture	Tenderness	Flavor
1	Cornstarch Water				
2	Flour Water				
3	Tapioca Water				
4	Cornstarch Water Sugar				
5	Cornstarch Lemon juice Water				
6	Cornstarch Milk				
7	Flour, browned Water				

*Note: Transparent, translucent, opaque.

Rice, Paste Products, and Cereals

OBJECTIVES

1. To prepare products of high starch content.
2. To continue the study of the behavior of starch in cookery where starch is the major component of the main food ingredient.
3. To demonstrate a method of cookery which retains the nutrients added to enriched rice and paste products.
4. To show volume increase in these starch-containing foods as a result of cooking.
5. To demonstrate methods of cereal cookery.

PRODUCTS TO BE PREPARED TO ILLUSTRATE PRINCIPLES

Rice pilaf
Hamburger skillet meal
Plain cooked rice, spaghetti, macaroni, noodles
Spaghetti with meat sauce
Baked macaroni in tomato sauce
Selected cereals

PRINCIPLES

*1. Water and heat must be present for gelatinization of starch.
2. Melted fat aids in separation of starch foods as well as in separating dry starch granules.
3. Gelatinized starch in cereals, rice, and paste products tends to be sticky (adhesive properties of cooked starch). Starch from ruptured starch granules can be removed by washing cooked rice or cooked paste products.
4. Gelatinization of starch in cereals, rice, and paste products causes an increase in volume.
5. Dextrinization of starch reduces amount of gelatinization.
6. Products high in starch tend to be bland in flavor.
7. Vitamins and minerals used to enrich rice, cereals, and paste products are water soluble.

*Ratio of water to starch is important.

97

CEREALS

Bulgar wheat (sometimes called **parboiled wheat**): whole wheat that has been cooked, dried, partly debranned, and cracked into coarse, angular fragments. Originated in the Near East.

    1. Prepare following directions on package.
    2. Record working time: _____ minutes.

Farina (granulated wheat endosperm): made from wheat other than durum with the bran and most of the germ removed. It is prepared by grinding and sifting the wheat to a granular form.

    1. Prepare following directions on package.
    2. Record working time: _____ minutes.

Oatmeal (rolled oats): made by rolling the groats (oats with hull removed) to form flakes. Regular oats and quick-cooking oats differ only in thinness of flakes. For quick-cooking oats, the finished groats (edible portion of the kernel) are cut into tiny particles which are then rolled into thin, small flakes. Instant oatmeal has been precooked.

    1. Prepare following directions on package.
    2. Record working time: _____ minutes.

Hominy grits (corn grits, grits): prepared from either white or yellow corn from which the bran and the germ have been removed. The remaining edible portion is ground and sifted. Grits are coarser than cornmeal.

    1. Prepare following directions on package.
    2. Record working time: _____ minutes.

Corn meal: prepared by grinding cleaned white or yellow corn to a fineness specified by federal standards. Corn meal may be *bolted* (further decreases size of granule); it may be *degerminated* (remove germ portion of kernel thus removing fat); it may be *enriched* (adds specified amounts of thiamine, riboflavin, niacin and iron—optional: calcium and vitamin D).

    1. Prepare following recipe on page 99.
    2. Record working time: _____ minutes.

CHARACTERISTICS OF HIGH QUALITY COOKED CEREALS
(Cereals to be evaluated while hot)

Appearance: Distinct particles, granules, or flakes.
Consistency: Thick; somewhat viscous (without gumminess).
Flavor: Bland (cooked starch); typical for grain (wheat, corn, oats); well-rounded (no raw starch).
Tenderness: Not evaluated for this product.
Mouth Feel: Particles remain discrete; soft.

Corn Meal Mush

Corn meal	1/2 cup	125 ml
Water, cold	1/2 cup	125 ml
Water, boiling	1 1/2 cups	375 ml
Salt	1/2 teaspoon	2 ml

1. Bring 1 1/2 cups (375 ml) water to boiling.
2. Blend the corn meal, salt, and cold water together.
3. Remove saucepan of boiling water from heat. Spoon or pour the corn meal-cold water mixture into the hot water, stirring until evenly blended.
4. Return saucepan to heat and bring corn meal mixture to a boil and boil for 5 minutes. Stir constantly. Be careful the hot cereal does not boil so vigorously that it spatters.
5. Reduce heat to lowest temperature. Cover saucepan and allow mush to heat for 10 minutes more.
6. Serve hot as a cereal or transfer cooked mush to small aluminum loaf pan to cool completely for fried mush. Cover.
7. Refrigerate until fried.
8. Record total working time:_____ minutes.

Fried Mush

Cooked mush slices	5 or 6	5 or 6
Hydrogenated shortening	1 tablespoon	15 ml

1. Heat a heavy frying pan until it is moderately hot. (A few drops of water will evaporate in 2 or 3 seconds). Spread melted fat evenly over the bottom of the frying pan. *Do not* allow fat to smoke!
2. Cut mush into slices 1/4 to 3/8 inch (0.6 to 1.0 cm) thick. Place slices in hot frying pan. Reduce heat to medium temperature. Fry mush until it is crisp and golden brown; this may take 10–15 minutes for each side.
3. Use pancake turner to turn slice. Add more shortening if necessary. Fry mush on second side until crisp and golden brown.
4. For class evaluation do not use syrup on mush.
5. Record total working time: _____ minutes.

CHARACTERISTICS OF HIGH QUALITY FRIED CORN MEAL MUSH

Appearance: Slices are golden brown on each side. Surfaces appear fairly dry.
Texture: *Exterior* crust is crisp.
Interior soft; thickness of slice determines degree of softness.
Flavor: Toasted corn; very slightly sweet.

Rice*

Rice, long grain	1/3 cup	75 ml
Water	7/8 cup	200 ml
Salt	1/4 teaspoon	1 ml
Butter or margarine	1/2 teaspoon	2 ml

1. Bring water to a boil. Add the salt and the butter.
2. Add the rice. Stir to make sure rice is not clumped together. (Stir with a fork.)
3. Reduce heat. Tightly cover saucepan. Finish cooking at a simmering temperature. Stir occasionally with a fork.
4. Cook until a rice kernel can be mashed between the fingers. Approximately 20 minutes. Do not rinse the rice before serving.
5. Measure the cooked rice to obtain increase in volume:
   1/3 cup raw rice yields_____ cup(s) cooked rice.
   75 ml raw rice yields_____ ml cooked rice.
6. Record total working time:_____ minutes.

*Plain cooked rice is served with Pork Chop Suey, page 141, Lamb Curry, page 150, and Japanese Vegetables with Chicken and Shrimp, page 180.

One-half cup (125 ml) uncooked rice can be substituted for the 3 ounces (625 ml) dry noodles in the Hamburger Skillet Meal, page 101.

CHARACTERISTICS OF HIGH QUALITY COOKED RICE

Appearance: Grains intact; white, translucent.
Texture: Grains firm, but tender; fluffy.
Flavor: Bland.

Basic Rice Pilaf**

Rice, long grain, uncooked	1/2 cup	125 ml
Margarine	2 teaspoons	10 ml
Liquid (chicken broth, water, tomato juice)	1 1/2 cups	375 ml
Salt	1/4 teaspoon	1 ml

1. Melt fat in saucepan; add dry rice; stir rice constantly with a fork until *very lightly* browned—more *creamy* than brown.
2. Add liquid and salt; bring to a boil; boil about 2 minutes; reduce heat to *low*.
3. Cover saucepan *tightly;* cook 25–30 minutes or until rice is tender and has absorbed the liquid; stir occasionally with a *fork*.
4. Record total working time:_____ minutes.

**Bulgur wheat may be substituted for the rice.
Either Rice or Bulgur Pilaf can be used as a substitute for potatoes in a meal.

Macaroni, Spaghetti, Noodles (Pasta)

Macaroni (elbow) or spaghetti	1/2 cup	57 g
Noodles	1/2 cup	33 g
Water	2 cups	500 ml
Salt	1/2 teaspoon	2 ml
Margarine	1 teaspoon	5 ml

1. Place water in a 2-quart (2L) saucepan. Add salt and margarine. Heat to boiling.
2. Add *one* of the paste products to the boiling salted water. Keep the product boiling vigorously during the cooking period. Stir with a fork every 3 to 4 minutes to keep pasta from sticking to saucepan. Cook with saucepan uncovered.
3. Cook until pasta is tender—approximately 15 minutes.
4. Drain pasta through strainer. Rinse with *hot* tap water.
5. Measure the cooked pasta to measure increase in volume:

Paste Product	Uncooked (dry) Volume	Cooked Volume
Macaroni	1/2 cup	_____ cup(s)
	125ml	_____ ml
Spaghetti	1/2 cup	_____ cup(s)
	125 ml	_____ ml
Noodles	1/2 cup	_____ cup(s)
	125 ml	_____ ml

6. Record total working time:_____ minutes.

CHARACTERISTICS OF HIGH QUALITY ALIMENTARY PASTES (PASTA)

Appearance: Distinct strands or pieces.
Tenderness: Tender; little resistance to bite.
Flavor: Bland; noodles may have a slight egg flavor.

Hamburger Skillet Meal

Ground beef	1/2 pound	250 ml
Margarine	1 tablespoon	15 ml
Onion, medium	1/2	1/2
Green pepper	1/2	1/2
Tomatoes, canned	1 cup	250 ml
Worcestershire sauce	1/2 teaspoon	2 ml
Salt	1/2 teaspoon	2 ml
Pepper	few grains	few grains
Noodles, dry, 3-inch (8 cm) lengths*	3 ounces	625 ml
Water	1 cup	250 ml
Tomato juice	1 cup	250 ml

1. Melt the fat in an electric frying pan; add the beef; brown the meat; stir occasionally.
2. Remove dry skin from onion; wash, dry and chop onion.
3. Wash green pepper; remove center core; rinse center cavity; dry; chop.
4. Add remaining ingredients except tomato juice and noodles; stir, heat to boiling.
5. Spread the uncooked noodles over the top; pour tomato juice *evenly* over the noodles; cover tightly and simmer for 30 minutes or until noodles are tender and have absorbed most of the liquid. Stir occasionally.
6. Record total working time:_____ minutes.

*One-half cup (125 ml) uncooked rice may be substituted.

Spaghetti with Meat Sauce

Ground beef	3/4 pound	375	ml
Olive oil or shortening	2 tablespoons	30	ml
Mushrooms, canned	4 ounces	125	ml
Garlic clove	1	1	
Onions, large	2	2	
Salt	1/2 teaspoon	2	ml
Pepper	1/8 teaspoon	0.5	ml
Tomato paste	1/2 cup	125	ml
Tomato juice	1 1/2 cups	375	ml
Bay leaf	1/2	1/2	
Spaghetti, dry 3-inch (8 cm) lengths	4 ounces	375 ml	
Italian type cheese, grated	1/2 cup	125	ml

1. Remove dry skin from onions; wash, dry, chop.
2. Remove dry skin from garlic clove; wash, dry, and impale with half a toothpick.
3. Melt fat in the bottom of a heavy frying pan; add ground beef, mushrooms, onions, salt, pepper, and garlic. With constant stirring, cook until meat is brown.
4. Add tomato paste, tomato juice, bay leaf, and stir. Simmer until thick; remove bay leaf and garlic.
5. Boil spaghetti in 2-3 quarts (2-3L) of boiling, salted water (1 teaspoon salt/quart water or 5 ml/L water) in an uncovered pan; cook until tender; pour off cooking water and rinse spaghetti in *hot* water; drain.
6. Place drained spaghetti on a large, heated platter. Pour sauce over the top. Serve with grated Italian type cheese (Parmesan or Romano).
7. Record total working time: _____ minutes.

Baked Macaroni in Tomato Sauce

Macaroni, elbow	4 ounces	300 ml
Tomatoes, canned	1 cup	250 ml
Onion, small	1/2	1/2
Peppercorns	2	2
Bay leaf	1/4	1/4
Salt	1/2 teaspoon	2 ml
Tomato paste	2 tablespoons	30 ml
Cheddar cheese, shredded	1 cup	250 ml
Fine bread crumbs	1/3 cup	75 ml
Margarine	2 tablespoons	30 ml

1. Preheat oven to 350°F (175°C).
2. Boil macaroni in 2-3 quarts (2-3 L) of boiling, salted water (1 teaspoon salt/quart water or 5 ml salt/L water) in an uncovered pan; cook until tender; pour off cooking water and rinse macaroni in *hot* water; drain; place in a well-greased casserole.
3. Remove dry skin from onion; wash, dry and slice onion into several thin slices.
4. Simmer tomatoes with onion, peppercorns, and bay leaf for 5 minutes; rub through a sieve. Add salt and tomato paste; stir.
5. Pour sauce over macaroni; add grated cheese. Lightly stir with fork.
6. Melt margarine in small pan, add crumbs and stir. Sprinkle evenly over macaroni mixture.
7. Bake in a 350°F (175°C) oven 20-30 minutes or until crumbs are browned.
8. Record total working time: _____ minutes.

REVIEW QUESTIONS

1. Define or explain each of the following terms:
   a. Starch
   b. Dextrins
   c. Maltose
   d. Glucose (dextrose)
   e. Amylose
   f. Amylopectin
   g. Dextrinization
   h. Hydration
   i. Hydrolysis
   j. Pregelatinized starch
   k. Waxy starch

2. a. Give the ratio of ingredients in each of the four types of white sauce.
   b. List the use(s) for each type of white sauce.

3. Explain each of the following procedures in terms of the principles of starch cookery:
   a. Mixing starch with melted fat.
   b. Heating to boiling over direct heat.
   c. Constant stirring when cooking on direct heat.
   d. In a lemon pie filling adding the lemon juice at the last step.

4. Give reasons why the following statement cannot be true. "An undercooked starch pudding can be brought to optimum thickness by cooling in the refrigerator."

5. On the following scale, rate the clarity of the pastes made from the three different starches with water.

   Opaque ◄·····················► Translucent ◄·····················► Transparent

6. Why is pasta rinsed with *hot* water after cooking?

7. Describe the characteristics of high quality:
   a. Chocolate pudding.
   b. Noodles.
   c. Rice.

8. Enriched rice is cooked in a small amount of water and is not rinsed after cooking. Explain why these procedures must be followed.

9. If you had to prepare a cooked cereal for breakfast, what principles of starch cookery would be applicable?

10. The following was taken from an evaluation sheet of samples of brown gravy:

    Appearance—2, lumpy.
    Consistency—2, thin and lumpy.
    Flavor—4, starchy.

    What principles were *not* observed to account for the poor quality of this gravy?

11. Explain effect of dry heat on starch:
    a. On the color.
    b. On the thickening properties.

12. a. If 2 tablespoons (30 ml) of flour and 1 cup (250 ml) of milk will make a medium white sauce, how much browned flour will be needed to make a gravy of the same thickness using 1 cup (250 ml) of milk?
    b. What factor would affect your answer to 12(a)?

13. Explain your observations made on the effect of boiling water on cornstarch or flour.

14. Why is the dry corn meal mixed with cold water in making corn meal mush?

15. a. Why is a high temperature, 425°F (220°C) used to fry corn meal mush?
    b. How does this influence the choice of fat used for frying?

16. What is the relationship between amount of stirring and the quality of oatmeal? Explain.

17. Why do "instant" cereals require so little preparation time?

Milk

OBJECTIVES

1. To acquaint the student with various selected factors which affect the stability of proteins:
   a. Homogenization process.
   b. Heat.
   c. Acid.
   d. Enzymes.
   e. Salts.
2. To get students to appreciate the fact that stability of milk proteins may be both desirable and undesirable.

PRODUCTS TO BE PREPARED TO ILLUSTRATE PRINCIPLES

Variety of milk products
Heated fresh, fluid milk
Acidified fresh, fluid milk
Enzyme coagulation of milk
Heated sweetened condensed milk
Acidified sweetened condensed milk
Cream of tomato soup

PRINCIPLES

1. Casein is coagulated (precipitated) by the action of acid and/or the rennet enzyme.
2. Lactoglobulin and lactalbumin are coagulated (precipitated) by the action of heat.
3. Lactose caramelizes at a relatively low temperature.
4. Starch "buffers" the action of acid on milk protein.
*5. Commercial processing methods for production of dried milk solids and evaporated milk require heating of milk to a temperature at which enzymes in milk are inactivated and bacteria in milk are destroyed.

*While dried milk powder may be free of bacteria as produced, great care must be taken by the manufacturer not to reintroduce microorganisms during subsequent handling and packaging. The user must also handle dried milk powder in a sanitary way to avoid reintroduction of microorganisms.

104

CHARACTERISTICS OF MILK AND CREAM

Product	*Per Cent Water	*Per Cent Fat	*Per Cent Protein	Appearance	Consistency	Flavor
Reconstituted dry milk solids	90	0.1	3.6			
Fresh skim milk	90	0.1	3.6			
Whole milk, plain or homogenized	87	3.0–4.0	3.5			
Evaporated milk	74	not less than 7.9	10.0			
Sweetened condensed milk	26	not less than 8.5	8.1			
Half and Half	80	11.5	3.1			
Heavy whipping cream	58	36.0	2.2			

*Typical composition.

Coagulation of Fresh Fluid Milk—By Heat

Milk   1/2 cup   125 ml

1. Place milk in a flameproof glass saucepan; place over low heat.
2. Heat slowly to 212°F (100°C). *Do not stir.* Remove from heat.
3. Observe and identify constituent of milk involved in each change:
   a. Formation of film on surface of milk.

   b. Precipitation on surface of saucepan.

   c. Caramelization on surface of saucepan.

Coagulation of Fresh Fluid Milk—By Acid

Milk   1 cup minus 1 tablespoon   235 ml
Vinegar or lemon juice   1 tablespoon   15 ml

1. Measure the milk in a glass measuring cup.
2. Measure the pH of plain milk with special tape: pH_____.
3. Add the vinegar or lemon juice. Stir quickly to blend the two liquids.
4. Allow the mixture to stand at least 5 minutes before testing for curd formation.
5. Measure the pH of the mixture with special tape: pH_____.
6. Observe and identify constituent in milk involved in curd formation.

Coagulation of Fresh Fluid Milk—By Enzyme

	Milk Temperature		Measure of Milk		Rennet Tablet	Water (cold)	
1. From refrigerator	42°F	6°C	1 cup	250 ml	1/2	1 teaspoon	5 ml
2. Heated to	110°F	43°C	1 cup	250 ml	1/2	1 teaspoon	5 ml
3. Heated to	212°F	100°C	1 cup	250 ml	1/2	1 teaspoon	5 ml

1. Set out 5 custard cups for each temperature of milk.
2. Dissolve tablet in cold water.
3. If milk is to be heated, heat to temperature indicated.
4. Add rennet solution to milk. Stir quickly to thoroughly blend.
5. Pour mixture immediately into 5 custard cups.
6. Allow to stand at room temperature for 10 minutes.
7. Refrigerate for 1 hour before evaluating.
8. Observe and record below:
   a. Which sample(s) form a gel structure?

   b. Why did some sample(s) not form a gel structure?

   c. Which protein is involved in the formation of the gel?

Coagulation of Sweetened Condensed Milk—By Heat

Sweetened condensed milk   1 can

*1. Pour the sweetened condensed milk into the upper section of a 1 1/2 quart (1.5L) double boiler.
2. Put water into lower section of double boiler; place upper section over water; cover.
3. Heat to boiling; continue boiling for 3 hours or until the sweetened condensed milk has formed a gel and has become caramel in color. Add boiling water to lower section as necessary. Do *not* let lower section become dry!
4. Observe:
   a. Browning.

   b. Heat coagulation.

*Alternate Method:
1. Remove one end of the can. Tightly cover the milk by pressing aluminum foil down over the top of the can.
2. Place can in a pan of water; water should be at half the height of the can. Cover the pan.
3. Place pan over medium heat; heat to boiling; continue boiling for 3 hours or until the milk has become caramel in color. Do *not* let pan become dry; add boiling water as necessary.

Coagulation of Sweetened Condensed Milk—By Acid

Sweetened condensed milk	1/2 can	1/2 can
Lemon juice	1/4 cup	50 ml

1. Gradually stir lemon juice into the sweetened condensed milk.
2. Allow the mixture to stand at least 10 minutes before cutting into it.
3. Observe:
   a. Thickening of milk during addition of lemon juice.

   b. Firmness of gel after standing.

Cream of Tomato Soup

Butter	1 tablespoon	15 ml
Flour	1 tablespoon	15 ml
Salt	1/4 teaspoon	1 ml
Milk	1/2 cup	125 ml
Tomato paste	1 tablespoon	15 ml
Tomato juice	2/3 cup	150 ml
Peppercorn, whole	1	1
Bay leaf	1/4	1/4
Onion, thin slice	1	1

1. Simmer together for 5 minutes the tomato juice, peppercorn, bay leaf and onion. Strain into glass measuring cup. Add tomato juice to bring to 2/3 cup (150 ml). Add tomato paste. Blend.
2. Make a white sauce by melting the fat in a saucepan, adding the flour and salt, and blending until smooth.
3. Add the milk gradually with constant stirring to form a smooth paste. Do not have over heat while adding the milk.
4. Return mixture to heat; bring to a boil with constant stirring.
5. Add the tomato juice *to* the white sauce.
6. Heat to serving temperature, but do *not* boil.
7. Record total working time:_____minutes.

CHARACTERISTICS OF HIGH QUALITY TOMATO SOUP

Appearance: Pale red-orange; all ingredients appear well blended.
Consistency: Comparable to "thin" cream; smooth throughout.
Flavor: Mild tomato should predominate; spice flavors should be noticeable but not strong enough to be identified.

Cheese

OBJECTIVES

1. To study factors inherent in production of a *natural* cheese.
2. To recognize the relationship between *natural* cheese and *process* cheese.
3. To recognize that the term *process* identifies a specific cheese product and is also a part of the name of several other processed cheese products.
4. To give the student the opportunity to compare quality characteristics for selected:
   a. Natural cheeses.
   b. Process cheese products.
5. To demonstrate the effect of emulsifiers on fat stability of cheeses exposed to heat.
6. To demonstrate the effect of heat:
   a. On the protein in cheese.
   b. On the milk sugar.

PRODUCTS TO BE STUDIED TO ILLUSTRATE PRINCIPLES

Natural cheeses: Cottage; Cream; Camembert; Blue; Swiss; Cheddar
Process cheeses: Process cheese; Process cheese food; Process cheese spread
Open-faced cheese sandwiches

PRINCIPLES

1. Casein is precipitated from milk by the interaction of rennet enzymes, acid, and calcium salts. Mild heat is required for the reaction.
2. The character of natural cheese is determined by:
   a. Moisture content of the finished cheese.
   b. Length of aging period.
      (1) Unripened cheese—not aged.
      (2) Ripened cheese—type of organism used.
         (a) Bacteria—some produce gas holes.
         (b) Mold—the mold becomes an integral part of the cheese.
3. Complex casein molecule is peptized during the ripening of natural cheese.
4. The distinctive flavor of each type of natural cheese is due to one or more of the following factors:
   a. The microorganisms used in ripening.
   b. Length of aging period.
   c. Heat and humidity during aging.
   d. Breakdown of protein and/or fat.
   e. Production of specific chemicals.

110

5. All process cheese products contain added emulsifiers to help hold milk fat in dispersion during the cooking of the cheese products.
6. Addition of water, milk, and/or milk products to process cheese products reduces the distinctive cheese flavor of the natural cheese used in the production of the process cheese product.
7. Cheese protein can be toughened or made rubbery by overheating during the cooking of cheese products.

CHEESE CLASSIFICATIONS WITH STANDARDS OF IDENTITY FOR SEVERAL TYPES

1. Natural cheese:
   a. Moisture content (*soft*—high moisture; *hard*—low moisture).
   b. Unripened or ripened.
   c. Type of bacteria or mold used in ripening to produce specific characteristics of appearance, texture, or flavor.
2. Process cheese products:
   a. Moisture content.
   b. Milk fat content.
   c. Addition of emulsifiers.
   d. Addition of other ingredients.
3. Imitation process cheese spread:
   a. No Standards of Identity have been written for this product.
   b. Any ingredient can be used as long as it is properly declared on the label.

STANDARDS OF IDENTITY—CODE OF FEDERAL REGULATIONS: TITLE 21: PART 133 DATED APRIL 1, 1983

Type	Moisture (%)	Fat (% on solids basis)	Special Information
Natural Cheeses			
Cottage	Not more than 80	Not less than 4	Salt, an acid, and a stabilizer may be added
Cream	Not more than 55	Not less than 33	May contain not more than 0.5% of specified emulsifier*
Camembert	No standard set	No standard set	———
Blue	Not more than 46	Not less than 50	Not less than 60 days old
Swiss	Not more than 41	Not less than 43	Not less than 60 days old
Cheddar	Not more than 39	Not less than 50	Not less than 60 days old; held at not more than 35° F.
Process Cheese Products			
Process	Not more than 43	Not less than 47	†Emulsifier
Process cheese food	Not more than 44	Not less than 23	†Emulsifier, milk, and/or milk products; spices, flavorings or other ingredients such as fruits, vegetables or meats.
**Process cheese spread	More than 44 but *not* more than 60	Not less than 20	†Emulsifier, milk, and/or milk products; spices, flavorings or other ingredients such as fruits, vegetables or meats.

*Where a Standard of Identity has been written for a product, no ingredient list is required *unless* the optional ingredients are used in which case ingredients must be listed on the label.

†Weight of solids of emulsifier cannot be more than 3% of the weight of the process cheese product. Emulsifiers may be one or a mixture of: disodium phosphate; sodium or potassium citrate; or others as listed.

**Product must be spreadable at 70° F.

CHEESE EVALUATION

Date: _____

Name	Natural or Processed	Moisture Content	Not Ripened or Ripened	Mold or Bacteria	Added Ingredients	Tenderness	Texture	Flavor	Comments

AFFECT OF HEAT ON NATURAL CHEESE AND PROCESS CHEESE PRODUCTS

Open-Faced Grilled Sandwiches

Bread—1 slice for each cheese product tested.
*Cheese slices—cut equally thick for each type; sufficient to cover bread.

1. Place a slice of bread for each cheese to be tested on a baking sheet. Arrange so that each slice of bread will receive equal heat from the broiler.
2. Arrange slices of cheese of one type on a slice of bread. Each sandwich may be cut into four pieces after broiling so each group member will have his portion for evaluation from the same basic sample.
3. Have the surface of the cheese 6–8 inches (15–20 cm) below the broiler element (or gas flame).
4. Broil the tray of sandwiches until the sampel of *process cheese* is just melted.
5. Remove tray from heat.
6. Cut samples for evaluation.

*Use following types of cheese: natural cheddar; process cheese; process cheese food; process cheese spread; imitation process cheese spread.

CHARACTERISTICS OF HIGH QUALITY OPEN-FACED GRILLED CHEESE SANDWICHES

Appearance: Bread—golden brown, even color; cheese—just barely melted; little or no browning.
Texture: Cheese—smooth, even.
Tenderness: Cheese—tender.
Flavor: Cheese—typical natural cheddar cheese—slightly tart, yet sweet flavor.

REVIEW QUESTIONS FOR MILK AND CHEESE

1. a. List the main constituents of milk (those constituents which contribute to its functional properties). Include the specific names of the three most important milk proteins.
   b. What action does the application of heat have on the carbohydrate and proteins?
   c. How does the addition of an acid affect the stability of each of the three proteins?

2. a. What are the optimum conditions for preparation of rennet desserts?
   b. Explain what happens if rennet dessert is prepared using milk at 150°F (65.5°C).
   c. Explain what happens if the milk is too cold.

3. List some food products containing milk in which the coagulation of milk:
   a. Would be undesirable.
   b. Is desirable or essential.

4. a. Why does sweetened condensed milk turn brown when heated?
   b. What happened to the consistency of the sweetened condensed milk when heated? Explain why this happened.

5. List and discuss the factors that determine the characteristics of natural cheese.

6. a. What happened to the cheddar cheese when it was heated in making the open-face cheese sandwich?
   b. Explain these observations.
   c. Which samples had the greatest tendency to brown?
   d. From your knowledge of the constituents of process cheese, explain your observations in part (c).

7. Define or explain the following terms:
   a. Sol.
   b. Gel.
   c. Gelation.
   d. Syneresis.
   e. Natural cheese.
   f. Process cheese.
   g. Standards of Identity.
   h. Peptization.
   i. pH (hydrogen ion concentration).

Eggs and Custards

OBJECTIVES

1. To illustrate and discuss quality characteristics of shell eggs:
   a. Fresh eggs.
   b. Frozen in the shell.
2. To illustrate selected methods for cooking.
3. To illustrate selected factors which affect the coagulation of egg protein.
4. To acquaint the student with differences between stirred (soft) and baked custards.

PRODUCTS TO BE PREPARED TO ILLUSTRATE PRINCIPLES

Fresh eggs (in shell and broken onto plate)
Egg frozen in shell
Baked custard
Stirred custard
Fried eggs
Scrambled eggs
Hard-cooked eggs
French (or plain) Cheese Omelet.

PRINCIPLES

1. Quality characteristics of shell eggs:
   a. Deteriorate with aging.
   b. Are dependent on storage conditions.
   c. Deteriorate with freezing in the shell.
2. Egg protein coagulates to form a gel structure by application of:
   a. Heat.
   b. Mechanical treatment.
3. Coagulation temperature of egg protein is affected by:
   a. Dilution.
   b. Sugar.
   c. Acid.
   d. Homogenization treatment of milk.
   e. Rate of heating.
4. Excessive heat treatment of the egg protein results in:
   a. Curdling.
   b. Syneresis.
   c. Toughening of the protein.

Basic Custard (See page 252 and 253 for Microwave Method.)

Milk	1 cup	250 ml
Egg, blended*	1 whole + 2 tablespoons	1 whole + 30 ml
Sugar	2 tablespoons	30 ml
Salt	few grains	few grains
Vanilla	1/4 teaspoon	1 ml

Nutmeg, if desired — a few grains on top of each custard to be baked

1. Preheat oven to 400°F (220°C).
2. Put 1 small sized custard cup in refrigerator to use at Step 12.
3. Blend together the milk, egg, sugar, and salt. Do not beat until the mixture becomes foamy. (The mixture may be strained before heating to remove chalazae.)

Baked Custard

4. Pour part of the mixture into one of the smallest custard cups. Cup should be filled to 1/2 inch (1.3 cm) from the top. Add 1/8 teaspoon (0.5 ml) vanilla; blend by stirring. Sprinkle a few grains of nutmeg on the top if desired.
5. Place the custard cup in a pan of warm water; water in the pan should be of same depth as custard in the custard cup. (For class several students can put custards in one baking pan.)
6. Place the pan of custards in the oven; reduce heat to 350°F (175°C).
7. Bake until a knife inserted near the center comes out clean (about 45 minutes).
8. Record total working time:_____minutes.

Stirred Custard

9. Put the custard mix remaining after Step 3 in the upper part of a double boiler. Have water in the lower part of the double boiler hot, but not boiling. Do not allow the water to boil during the cooking period.
10. Stir custard constantly during cooking; use wooden spoon; custard must be cooked *slowly*, 15–25 minutes.
11. Cook until the custard coats a metal spoon. (At this stage the custard clings to the spoon in a coating about half the thickness of a chocolate coating on a candy bar.)
12. Pour the cooked custard *immediately* into a cold serving dish. It is essential to stop the cooking process *quickly* to prevent the custard from curdling.
13. Add 1/8 teaspoon (0.5 ml) vanilla. Stir until well-blended.
14. Record total working time:_____minutes.

*Quantity of egg has been increased to reduce baking time to accommodate a 110 minute laboratory period. One egg + 1 cup (250 ml) milk will form a firm gel structure, but require a longer baking period.

CHARACTERISTICS OF HIGH QUALITY BAKED CUSTARDS

Appearance: Pale golden brown surface.
Consistency: Even gel structure which holds a clear, sharp cut edge.
Flavor: Nutmeg may mask slight egg flavor.

CHARACTERISTICS OF HIGH QUALITY STIRRED CUSTARDS

Appearance: Pale yellow dependent on color of egg yolks.
Consistency: Consistency of heavy cream before the cream is whipped; smooth.
Flavor: Bland, slightly sweet, slight egg flavor; vanilla may mask egg flavor.

Observations of Quality of Raw Eggs Out of Shell

Eggs as available—1 egg per student

1. Break egg out onto a flat plate 6–7 inches (15–18 cm) diameter, white preferred. Before discarding the shell, observe the depth of the air cell in the large end of the egg shell as an indication of deterioration: the larger the air cell, the greater is the degree of deterioration.
2. Avoid moving the egg around on the plate as much as possible to minimize damage to the egg before it can be evaluated for quality.
3. If models of graded eggs are available, compare the fresh egg with the models; otherwise, compare the fresh egg with photographs of graded eggs.

CHARACTERISTICS OF HIGH QUALITY RAW EGGS OUT OF SHELL*

Appearance:
Yolk: Will stand up high and firm above the egg white; diameter will be relatively small; yolk should be fairly well centered in the egg white.
White: Will have a high ratio of thick, firm, white; thick white will also stand up; white will be free from meat spots or blood spots; white may be somewhat translucent.
Odor: Mild egg aroma.

*Where possible, compare egg out of shell with Grade Models of eggs and/or marketing charts depicting characteristics of egg quality.

Frozen Egg in the Shell

1. Place one or more shell eggs in a freezer; the shell is apt to crack, so the eggs should be placed in a container during freezing. The eggs must remain in the freezer long enough to be thoroughly frozen (24 hours).
2. Remove the frozen eggs from the freezer several hours before the eggs are to be observed and discussed. Place the eggs in a glass custard cup so the amount of leakage during thawing can be observed.
3. Observe crack in the shell and leakage of egg white before breaking egg out onto a plate.
4. Break egg out onto a plate 6–7 inches (15–18 cm) diameter, white preferred. Observe the following:

Egg white
1. Physical breakdown of egg white.
2. White is thin, watery, and breaks away from the egg yolk.
3. Whipping properties, however, have not been affected.

Egg yolk
1. Firmness, rubberiness, and pastiness are a result of chemical "binding" of water during freezing.
2. Yolk loses its ability to blend with other ingredients.

Hard-Cooked Eggs

Eggs, room temperature—4 or 5

1. Use enough water in saucepan so the water completely covers the eggs in the shell during the cooking period.
2. Bring the water to a boil.
3. Place the eggs in the shell on a tablespoon to set into the boiling water. At the time eggs are added, heat should be reduced so water is no longer actively boiling.
*4. Cook the eggs at a simmering temperature, 185°–200°F (85°–93°C) for about 20–25 minutes. Original temperature of the eggs, number of eggs cooked at one time, and the temperature at which the eggs are cooked will all influence the time necessary to produce a high quality hard-cooked egg.
5. At the end of the cooking period, allow cold tap water to flow over the eggs until the eggs feel cool, about 5 minutes.
6. Remove eggs from water; dry shells; remove shells.
7. Record total working time:_____ minutes.

*To compare the effect of temperature fo cooking on the quality of hard-cooked eggs, prepare a second sample at a rolling boil for as long as the first sample is simmered.

CHARACTERISTICS OF HIGH QUALITY HARD-COOKED EGGS

Appearance: Yolk should be evenly centered in the egg white; yolk should have the same color on its exterior surface and its interior cut edge (no dark ring); yolk should have even consistency throughout—it appears mealy and dry.
Texture: Yolk should be dry and mealy.
Tenderness: White is firm enough to hold together, yet is only slightly resistant to bite.
Flavor: Mild to bland egg flavor.

Fried Eggs

Egg	1	1
Butter or margarine	1 teaspoon	5 ml
Water	1 tablespoon	15 ml

1. Melt butter or margarine in small frying pan.
2. Break the egg out of its shell onto a small saucer. Slide the egg into the hot (but not smoking) fat.
3. Add the water. Cover frying pan *immediately* with a tight-fitting lid.
4. Allow the steam until the white is opaque and the yolk is partially coagulated. (Yolk should still be somewhat runny).
5. Record total working time:_____ minutes.

CHARACTERISTICS OF HIGH QUALITY FRIED EGGS

Appearance: Yolk is covered with a film of coagulated egg white; coagulated egg white is opaque and shiny.
Consistency: Egg yolk should be slightly fluid; the egg white has coagulated to form a firm gel structure.
Tenderness: Egg white is tender and shows very little resistance to cutting or chewing.
Flavor: Mild egg flavor; if butter has been used, butter flavor may enhance the egg flavor.

Scrambled Eggs (See page 252 for Microwave Method.)

Eggs	2	2
Milk	2 tablespoons	30 ml
Butter or margarine	1 teaspoon	5 ml
Salt	1/4 teaspoon	1 ml
Pepper, white (if desired)	few grains	few grains

1. Place the eggs in a bowl; add the milk and seasonings.
2. Blend ingredients with a rotary beater until well blended but *not* foamy.
3. Melt the butter or margarine in a heavy frying pan.
4. Add the egg mixture to the hot (not smoking) fat.
5. Stir the egg mixture *occasionally*; use pancake turner for this; *do not* overcook; the eggs continue to cook slightly after they are removed from the frying pan.
6. Record total working time:_____minutes.

CHARACTERISTICS OF HIGH QUALITY SCRAMBLED EGGS

Appearance: Egg masses appear slightly moist and creamy; *usually* egg masses are large.
Consistency: Even consistency throughout; all liquid is held by coagulated protein.
Tenderness: Egg masses are tender and have little resistance when cut or chewed.
Flavor: Mild egg flavor; butter flavor will enhance egg flavor.

French (or Plain) Cheese Omelet

Eggs	2	2
Milk	2 tablespoons	30 ml
Butter or margarine	2 teaspoons	10 ml
Salt	1/4 teaspoon	1 ml
Pepper, white (if desired)	few grains	few grains
Sharp cheddar cheese, grated*	2 tablespoons	30 ml

1. Place eggs in a bowl with milk and seasonings.
2. Beat with a rotary beater until blended, but not foamy.
3. Melt butter in a 6 or 8 inch (15–20 cm) omelet pan or frying pan.
4. Add egg mixture to hot (not smoking) fat.
5. As the egg begins to coagulate around the edges of the pan, gently lift the eggs with metal spatula to allow liquid egg to flow on to the surface of the frying pan. Do *not* break up the coagulated mass. Keep working uncooked portion of egg onto the omelet pan. Keep heat low enough so egg does not burn on bottom. Surface of egg will appear quite moist although coagulated.
6. Sprinkle grated cheese over half the top of the omelet.
7. Gently fold remaining half of omelet over the cheese.
8. Ease the folded omelet onto a serving plate.
9. Record total working time:_____ minutes.

*Finely chopped, cooked ham could be substituted. A cooked vegetable such as asparagus, spinach, or broccoli could be substituted for the cheese and a cheese sauce, page 177, could be served over the omelet. Combinations of the above may also be used.

CHARACTERISTICS OF HIGH QUALITY FRENCH OR PLAIN CHEESE OMELET

Appearance: Surface of omelet is golden brown. Omelet retains its shape.
Consistency: Surface is firm; center egg mass is slightly moist and creamy; cheese may not be completely melted.
Tenderness: Surface may show slight resistance when cut. Center portion has little resistance when cut or chewed.
Flavor: Mild egg flavor blended with distinct cheese flavor (or a distinct ham or vegetable used as a substitute).

Egg Foams

OBJECTIVES

1. To prepare selected food products based on egg white foam structure.
2. To illustrate and discuss stages of foam formation.
3. To illustrate selected factors which affect:
   a. Rate of foam formation.
   b. Stability of egg white foams.

PRODUCTS TO BE PREPARED TO ILLUSTRATE PRINCIPLES

Angel cake
Sponge cake
Demonstration of stages of foam formation
Jelly roll
Cheese souffle
Prune whip
Floating island

PRINCIPLES

1. Foam structure depends on a gas (air) to be dispersed throughout a liquid that contains a third constituent having the ability to become rigid at the gas/liquid interface (point of contact).
2. Egg white protein gives rigidity to the foam structure as a result of partial coagulation.
3. Temperature of egg white affects the amount of work necessary for foam formation.
4. Stability of egg white foam is dependent on:
   a. Quality of eggs.
   b. Degree of beating.
   c. Addition of sugar:
      (1) Amount added.
      (2) Time of addition of sugar in relation to stage of beating.
   d. Addition or presence of fat.
   e. Addition of acid:
      (1) Time of addition of acid in relation to stage of beating.
      (2) Amount of acid added.

STAGES OF FRESH EGG WHITE FOAM FORMATION

1. **Foamy:**
   a. Bubbles form on the surface, but not all of the white is broken up.
   b. Foam is extremely unstable.
   c. Air cells are variable in size but are generally quite large.
   d. Mixture is still fluid.
   e. Mixture starts to become opalescent.

   Acid, salt, and vanilla are added at this stage.

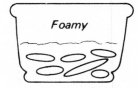

2. **Soft Peaks:**
   a. Air cells are medium fine; all of the white exists as foam.
   b. Foam is fairly stable; slight drainage upon short standing.
   c. Mixture is shiny; flows readily in bowl.
   d. Mass is elastic.
   e. Soft peaks fall over to near the base of the foam as beater is lifted from foam.

   To obtain optimum volume, sugar is added gradually, but quickly, to prevent peptization of egg albumen by sugar at this stage and to reduce the possibility of overbeating.

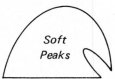

3. **Stiff Peaks:**
   a. Air cells are fine, especially if acid has been added at the foamy stage; mixture is very white and opaque.
   b. Foam is quite stable (even if plain egg whites); some drainage will occur with prolonged standing.
   c. Mixture is shiny; flows slowly in bowl.
   d. Mass is still elastic.
   e. Peaks are still quite soft, but only the tip of the peak falls over as the beater is pulled from the foam.

   Egg whites for souffles and omelets are beaten to this stage. Egg whites and sugar are beaten to this stage for angel cakes and pie meringues in order to retain elasticity.

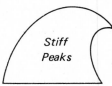

4. **Dry:**
   a. Air cells are very fine; mixture is extremely white.
   b. Foam is not stable; drainage occurs rapidly on standing.
   c. Mixture is dull; it has lost its ability to flow in the bowl.
   d. Mass is brittle and inelastic; peaks remain in rigid points.

   This stage is generally to be avoided for products using fresh egg whites.
   Reconstituted, dehydrated egg whites must be beaten to this stage for all products including commercial angel cake mixes.

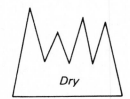

Angel Cakes

Egg whites, 2	1/4 cup	60	ml
Cream of tartar	1/8 teaspoon	0.5	ml
Salt	1/8 teaspoon	0.5	ml
Sugar	1/4 cup + 1 tablespoon	65	ml
Cake flour	1/4 cup	60	ml
Vanilla	1/8 teaspoon	0.5	ml

1. Preheat oven to 350°F (175°C).
2. Sift 1 tablespoon (15 ml) of sugar with the flour.
3. Beat egg whites until foamy.
4. Add cream of tartar, salt, and vanilla. Continue beating until soft peaks form.
5. Add remaining sugar in approximately 5 portions to the beaten egg whites. Beat 6–8 revolutions of the beater after each addition of sugar. Use a *hand mixer. Do not overbeat.* The egg white-sugar mixture should have the consistency of a pie meringue with stiff peaks.
6. Add the flour mixture in four approximately equal portions to the egg white-sugar mixture. The flour will fold in easier if it is sifted over the top of the egg white meringue. Fold the flour into the egg whites using a metal spatula. *Do not overblend.*
*7. Use the rubber spatula to push the batter into an ungreased baking pan approximately 5 X 3 1/4 X 2 1/2 inches (12 X 8 X 6 cm).
8. Bake for 25 to 30 minutes in an oven preheated to 350°F (175°C). The top will spring back when lightly pressed with the finger.
9. Invert cake on cake rack to cool.
10. Record total working time: _____ minutes.

*If pans the size described are unavailable, the recipe above can be doubled and baked in a 6 or 7 inch (15 or 18 cm) tube pan.

CHARACTERISTICS OF HIGH QUALITY ANGEL CAKES

Appearance: Top crust is slightly rounded; top crust is golden brown to medium brown; surface may be rough and slightly cracked.

Texture: Air cells may vary in size from small to medium; cell walls should be fairly thin.

***Tenderness:** Crumb is tender; the crumb "melts" in the mouth—very little resistance to bite.

Flavor: Flavor is slightly sweet; vanilla and/or almond flavor may be detected. Small cakes baked and evaluated within a 2-hour period may have a distinct eggy flavor; this eggy flavor is lost as the cake stands for several hours.

*In foam cakes, tenderness is a more important characteristic than texture (size of air cells).

Sponge Cake

Eggs, separated	4	4
Sugar	2/3 cup	150 ml
Lemon juice	2 teaspoons	10 ml
Water	1 tablespoon	15 ml
Salt	1/4 teaspoon	1 ml
Lemon rind, grated	1/2 teaspoon	2 ml
Cake flour	2/3 cup	150 ml

1. Preheat oven to 350°F (175°C).
2. The sugar is to be divided into approximately three equal portions. One portion will be added at *Step 3*; one portion at *Step 6*; and the last portion at *Step 8*.
3. Sift one portion of the sugar with the cake flour and salt.
4. Combine the water and the lemon juice.
5. In small bowl beat the egg yolks with electric mixer until the yolks are very thick and lemon colored. Soft peaks should begin to form. Add lemon rind.
6. With continuous beating add one of the portions of sugar, about 1 teaspoonful (5 ml) at a time, alternately with the lemon juice-water mixture (1 teaspoonful or 5 ml at a time). After each addition of sugar or liquid, beat the egg yolks back to a light foam before further additions. Peaks will remain quite soft, but the yolk-sugar mixture should have the consistency of mayonnaise dressing.
7. Add the flour-sugar mixture a *tablespoonful* (15 ml) at a time by folding it in with a metal spatula. *Do not overblend.*
8. Use a hand beater to beat the egg whites until soft peaks form. Gradually add the last portion of sugar about 1 teaspoon (5 ml) at a time, turning the handle of the beater 6 to 8 times after each addition. *Do not overbeat.* The egg white-sugar mixture should be beaten until stiff peaks are formed.
9. Add the egg yolk-flour mixture to the egg white meringue. Fold the two mixtures together with a metal spatula. *Do not overblend.*
10. Use the rubber spatula to push the batter into an ungreased tube pan 6 or 7 inches (15–18 cm) in diameter.
11. Bake for 25–30 minutes in an oven preheated to 350°F (175°C). The top crust should spring back when lightly pressed with the finger.
12. Invert cake on cake rack for cooling.
13. Record total working time:_____minutes.

CHARACTERISTICS OF HIGH QUALITY SPONGE CAKES

Appearance: Top is slightly rounded; top crust is light golden brown; surface may be rough and slightly cracked.

Texture: Air cells are fairly small and uniformly distributed; cell walls are fairly thin.

*Tenderness: Crumb is tender with slight resistance to bite.

Flavor: A delicate lemon flavor should predominate when grated lemon rind and fresh lemon juice are used; a slight egg flavor can be detected if the lemon rind and lemon juice are not used; a slightly sweet flavor is apparent.

*In foam cakes, tenderness is a more important characteristic than texture (size of air cells).

Jelly Roll

Eggs, separated	3	3
Sugar	1 cup	250 ml
Water	1/4 cup	50 ml
Vanilla	1 teaspoon	5 ml
Cake flour	1 cup	250 ml
Baking powder	1 teaspoon	5 ml
Salt	1/4 teaspoon	1 ml
Confectioner's sugar	1/2 cup	125 ml
Raspberry jam	3/4 cup	175 ml

1. Preheat oven to 375°F (190°C).
2. Sift together cake flour, baking powder, salt, and 2 tablespoons (30 ml) of the sugar.
3. Blend water and vanilla.
4. In a small bowl beat the egg yolks with electric mixer until the yolks are very thick and lemon colored. Soft peaks should begin to form.
5. With continuous beating add about 7 tablespoons (100 ml) of remaining sugar, 1 teaspoonful (5 ml) at a time, alternately with 1 teaspoonful (5 ml) vanilla-water mixture. After each addition of sugar or water, beat the egg yolks back to a light foam before further additions. Peaks will remain quite soft, but the yolk-sugar mixture should have the consistency of mayonnaise dressing.
6. Sift one fourth of the flour mixture over the egg yolk mixture. Fold in with approximately 15 strokes using a metal spatula.
7. Repeat Step 6 until all of the flour has been added.
8. Beat egg whites until soft peaks form.
9. With continuous beating add last of sugar, approximately 7 tablespoons, (100 ml) gradually but quickly to the beaten egg whites. Beat until stiff peaks are formed. *Do not overbeat* egg whites after the addition of the sugar.
10. Pour the egg yolk-flour mixture over the beaten egg white-sugar mixture. Fold the two mixtures together *lightly* until ingredients are just blended.
11. Grease a 15 1/2 × 10 1/2-inch (39 × 26 cm) jelly roll pan (bottom only). Line the bottom with brown paper. Grease the brown paper.
12. Pour the batter into the prepared baking pan. Bake in a 375°F (190°C) oven for 12–15 minutes or until the top springs back when lightly touched.
13. Sift confectioner's sugar on a clean towel the dimensions of the baking pan.
14. As soon as the cake is removed from the oven, loosen edges, then turn cake out onto the confectioner's sugar. Carefully remove the paper. Trim 1/2 inch (1.5 cm) off all four sides. Use serated cake knife with a sawing motion.
15. While the cake is still hot, starting at the narrow end, roll cake and towel together. The towel should hold the cake in position until the cake has cooled.
16. When the cake is cold, carefully open up the towel and unroll the cake. If the cake is warm when the filling is added, the filling soaks into the cake.
17. Carefully spread the cake with filling (red raspberry jam). *Do not* spread filling on the last inch (2.5 cm) of the narrow end of the cake toward which the cake will be rolled. The jam tends to spread out as the cake is rolled, so filling will fill this area. Be sure the filling is at the edges of the cake on the long sides of the cake. The filling should be soft, easily spreadable, but not wet or syrupy.
18. Carefully reroll the cake. Cut into 1-inch (2.5 cm) slices for serving.
19. Record total working time: _____ minutes.

CHARACTERISTICS OF HIGH QUALITY JELLY ROLLS

Appearance: Cake evenly browned, crumb lemon yellow (depending on color of egg yolk); any frosting or covering evenly distributed; filling even.
Texture: Air cells small (slightly larger than sponge cake), evenly distributed; cell walls fairly thin.
Tenderness: Crumb tender, slightly resilient to bite (a bit elastic—not "short").
Flavor: Cake—sweet, and slightly eggy. Filling—evenly balanced; typical of the food product used.

Cheese Souffle

Flour, all-purpose	2 tablespoons	30 ml
Salt	1/4 teaspoon	1 ml
Milk	2/3 cup	150 ml
Margarine	1 tablespoon	15 ml
Cheddar cheese, shredded	3/4 cup	175 ml
Cayenne pepper	few grains	few grains
Eggs, separated	2	2

1. Preheat oven to 350°F (175°C).
2. Blend the flour, salt, and cayenne pepper together in a saucepan. Add the cold milk gradually and stir until the flour is evenly dispersed.
3. Place on heat and bring quickly to a boil with constant stirring. Boil 1 minute until the sauce is thick. Remove from heat.
4. Add the butter and shredded cheese to the hot sauce. Stir until the cheese has melted. (This mixture should appear well blended.)
5. Add the unbeaten egg yolks to the sauce; stir until eggs are well blended.
6. Beat the egg whites until they begin to form stiff peaks; the peaks should still bend *slightly*. Have the egg whites in a bowl large enough to add the sauce mixture.
7. Add the sauce mixture to the egg whites; fold with a metal spatula until all ingredients are blended. *Fold lightly. Do not overblend.*
*8. Lightly butter the *bottom* of a small size (1-quart or 1-L) baking dish. Pour in souffle mixture. Set the dish in a pan of warm water—the water should be the same depth as the amount of souffle in its baking dish.
9. Place in a 350°F (175°C) oven and bake until a knife inserted in the center comes out "clean."†
10. Record total working time:_____minutes.

*For class, bake these products in individual glass baking dishes (lightly butter the *bottom* of 4 or 5 of the smallest size glass baking dishes). Bake in pans of water as indicated above.

†Approximate baking times: small cups, 30-35 minutes; quart baking dish, 50 minutes.

CHARACTERISTICS OF HIGH QUALITY CHEESE SOUFFLES

Appearance: Dark golden brown top crust; top is generally uneven.
Texture: Even distribution of medium-small gas holes; medium thick to fine cell walls; mixture is homogeneous.
Tenderness: Very little resistance when cut; "melts" in the mouth.
Flavor: Mild cheese.

Baked Prune Whip

Prune pulp	1/2 cup	125 ml
Sugar	3 tablespoons	45 ml
Salt	1/8 teaspoon	0.5 ml
Lemon juice	2 teaspoons	10 ml
Egg whites	2	2

1. Preheat oven to 350°F (175°C).
2. Stewed prunes should be drained and pitted. The pulp should be rather dry. Cut the pulp into several pieces for each prune. Place in a bowl large enough for all ingredients after beating.
3. Add the egg whites, salt, and lemon juice. Beat with electric mixer until stiff peaks are formed.
4. Add the sugar gradually with continued beating.
*5. Pile lightly into a baking dish (butter bottom only). Set dish in pan of warm water.
6. Bake in a 350°F (175°C) oven for 45 minutes or until the center is firm to the touch when pressed lightly with the forefinger.
7. Prune whip may be served with soft (stirred) custard.
8. Record total working time:_____ minutes.

*For class, bake these products in individual glass baking dishes (lightly butter the *bottom* of 4 or 5 of the smallest sized glass baking dishes). Bake in pans of water as indicated above.

CHARACTERISTICS OF HIGH QUALITY BAKED PRUNE WHIPS

Appearance: Dark golden brown to light brown top crust; top is generally uneven with some peaks.
Texture: Even distribution of medium-small gas holes; medium thick to thin cell walls; pieces of prune pulp may be evident.
Tenderness: Top crust may be slightly tough to cut through; interior is tender; little resistance to cutting or chewing.
Flavor: Mild prune with possible suggestion of lemon flavor; slightly sweet.

Floating Island (See page 253 for Microwave Method.)

*Meringue:

Egg whites	2	2
Sugar, finely granulated	1/4 cup	50 ml
Vanilla	1/4 teaspoon	1 ml

1. Preheat oven to 350°F (175°C).
2. Place egg whites into smallest size bowl. Add vanilla. Beat with rotary beater until the whites will form soft peaks as the beater is pulled from the foam.
3. Add the sugar gradually, beating only enough after each addition to blend sugar with foam. At the end of the beating period the egg whites should form fairly stiff peaks which slightly bend over at the tips.
4. Place 1/2 inch (1.5 cm) of hot water in a 9 × 13 inch (22 × 32 cm) pan.
5. Place the meringue on the *hot* water using a teaspoon to form 10 "islands."
6. Bake in a 350°F (175°C) oven until the meringue is set and the tips are golden brown—approximately 20 minutes.
7. Use slotted pancake turner to remove "islands" from the hot water onto a plate for cooling.
8. Place cooled "islands" on cooled soft custard for serving.
9. Record total working time:_____minutes.

   *This recipe may be used for the meringue on cream pies. Stop after step 3; spread meringue on cooled pie filling; brown meringue in 350°F (175°C) oven for 15-20 minutes.

†Custard:

Milk	1 1/2 cups	375 ml
Egg yolks	2	2
Egg, whole	1	1
Sugar	1/4 cup	50 ml
Vanilla	1/2 teaspoon	2 ml

1. Prepare a stirred custard from the custard ingredients (page 118).

   †The color of the custard will be more yellow and the consistency will be softer when egg yolks are used.

CHARACTERISTICS OF HIGH QUALITY FLOATING ISLANDS

Stirred Custard: See page 119.

Meringue

Appearance: Top is golden brown with peaks slightly darker; top surface is uneven.
Texture: Even distribution of small gas holes; cell walls are thin.
Tenderness: Top crust may be slightly tough to cut through; interior is easily cut with a knife and leaves a clean-cut edge.
Flavor: Mild, sweet.

REVIEW QUESTIONS

1. a. List the factors upon which eggs are *graded* for quality.
    b. Describe the characteristics of a high quality raw egg when it is broken out on a plate.
2. a. Describe the characteristics of the egg white and egg yolk from the egg frozen in the shell.
    b. Explain what happens to the constituents of the yolk and white to account for your observations.
3. Define and/or identify each of the following terms:
    a. Semipermeable membrane.
    b. Air cell.
    c. Vitelline membrane.
    d. Chalazae.
    e. Curdling.
    f. Syneresis.
    g. Ferrous sulfide.
4. Write the recipe for a basic custard mix.
5. How would each of the following changes affect the coagulation temperatures of a custard? Explain your answer.
    a. Increase the amount of sugar in the recipe.
    b. Substitute two egg yolks for one whole egg.
    c. Increase the amount of milk in the recipe.
6. a. Describe the changes in state (physical changes) of a stirred custard as it is heated.
    b. Differentiate between rate of heating and coagulation temperature.
    c. How will the rate of heating affect the coagulation temperature in making a stirred custard?
7. Why are baked custards, souffles, and whips baked with the container placed in a pan of water?
8. Why does a beaten whole egg give less volume than the egg white alone?
9. Formation of egg white foams:
    a. List the four stages of beating a fresh egg white foam.
    b. At what stage is cream of tartar added? Why?
    c. At what stage is sugar added? Why?
10. Foam-type cakes:
    a. What is the leavening agent in cakes of this type?
    b. What are the structural ingredients?
    c. How does the term "extensible protein" apply to these cakes?
    d. How does the temperature of the egg white affect foam formation?
    e. What are the functions of cream of tartar in the angel cake recipe?
    f. Why are foam cakes cooled in the inverted position?
    g. How is it possible to overdevelop gluten in preparing an angel cake?
11. Why should foams be beaten *only* at the time they are to be used?
12. One student evaluated his products as shown in the evaluation table on the next page.

Explain the treatment each product received to account for this student's evaluations.

Quality Characteristic	Fried Egg	Angel Cake	Stirred Custard	Hard Cooked Eggs
Appearance	3 — Dark brown around edges	4 — Slightly dark	5	3 — Raw in center
Consistency or Texture	3 — White is lacy; yolk O.K.	2 — Many large air cells; cell walls thick	2 — Like milk	3 — Center of yolk not coagulated
Tenderness	3 — White tough; yolk O.K.	2 — Tough	--	3 — Too tender
Flavor	4 — Slight burned	4 — Sweet; sugary	4 — Eggy	4 — Raw
Overall Eating Quality	3	2	2	3

Starch-Egg Combinations

OBJECTIVES

1. To combine selected principles of starch cookery with selected principles of egg protein cookery in the preparation of a food product.
2. To review principles of starch cookery.
3. To review principles of egg protein cookery.
4. To relate temperature of coagulation of egg protein to temperature of maximum gelatinization of starch in preparation of a pudding or cream pie filling.

PRODUCTS TO BE PREPARED TO ILLUSTRATE PRINCIPLES

Creamy tapioca pudding
Lemon pudding or pie filling
Creamy cornstarch pudding or pie filling
Fruit salad dressing (see page 213)

PRINCIPLES

1. Starch granules are separated by dry ingredients and cold liquid for even gelatinization.
2. Starch mixtures are stirred constantly during cooking for even gelatinization of starch granules.
3. Starch mixtures are heated to boiling temperature to obtain maximum gelatinization.
4. Gelatinized starch may be hydrolyzed when boiled with acid resulting in loss of thickening properties.
5. Temperature of coagulation of egg protein may be 27–45°F (15–25°C) lower than temperature for maximum gelatinization of starch.
6. Egg protein acts as a thickening agent.
7. Egg protein may be peptized when boiled with acid.

Lemon Pudding

Water	1 cup	250	ml
Sugar	1 cup	250	ml
Cornstarch	3 tablespoons	45	ml
Salt	1/8 teaspoon	0.5	ml
Egg yolk	1	1	
Margarine	1 tablespoon	15	ml
Lemon juice	3 tablespoons	45	ml
Lemon rind, grated	1 teaspoon	5	ml

1. Set out 4 small custard cups or one 6-inch (15 cm) baked pie shell.
2. Combine approximately 3/4 of both water and sugar in a 1–1 1/2 quart (1–1.5 L) saucepan.
3. Add grated lemon rind.
4. Bring mixture to a boil; boil 1 minute; stir until sugar is dissolved.
5. Blend cornstarch and salt with remaining sugar; add remaining water; blend.
6. Blend 1 tablespoon (15 ml) of the hot water-sugar mixture with the cornstarch-sugar mixture. Repeat 2 times.
7. Add all of starch mixture to remaining hot water mixture. Blend.
8. Place over heat; bring to boil; boil 1 minute; stir constantly. Remove from heat.
9. Place egg yolk in a pint (500 ml) bowl; stir with fork until blended.
10. Add approximately 1 tablespoon (15 ml) hot starch paste to egg yolk. Blend thoroughly. Repeat 2 times.
11. Add egg mixture to remaining starch mixture. Blend thoroughly. Observe shiny quality due to raw egg.
12. Carefully heat egg-starch mixture over medium heat for 3 to 4 minutes with constant stirring. This mixture must *not* boil. When egg has coagulated the mixture will not be as shiny as at step 11. Stir in the lemon juice and margarine; continue stirring until mixture is smooth.
13. Pour into serving dishes.
14. This recipe serves 4 as a pudding or will make filling for one 6-inch (15 cm) pie.
15. Record total working time:_____ minutes.

Lemon Meringue or Cream Pie

1 6-inch (15 cm) baked pastry shell	Page 72
1 Recipe Lemon or Creamy Cornstarch Pudding	Page 134 or 135
1/2 Recipe Meringue	Page 130

1. Pour cooled filling into a cold, baked pastry shell.
2. Spread meringue to completely cover filling and touch edge of pastry.
3. Bake in a 350°F (175°C) oven for 20–30 minutes or until meringue is golden.

Pie should be evaluated on High Quality Characteristics for Pastry Shell (page 72), Starch-Egg Products (page 136) and Meringues (page 130) as well as for its Overall Eating Quality.

Creamy Cornstarch Pudding

Milk	1 cup	250	ml
Sugar	1/4 cup	50	ml
Salt	1/8 teaspoon	0.5	ml
Cornstarch	2 tablespoons	30	ml
Egg yolk	1	1	
Margarine or butter	1 tablespoon	15	ml
Vanilla	1/2 teaspoon	2	ml

1. Set out two small custard cups or one 6-inch (15 cm) baked pie shell.
2. Blend cornstarch, sugar, and salt in a 1 or 1 1/2 quart (1–1.5 L) saucepan.
3. Add milk in portions; stir after each addition until mixture is free of lumps.
4. Place saucepan over medium heat and stir constantly; bring to a boil and boil 1 minute; remove from heat.
5. Place egg yolk in a 2 or 3 cup (500–750 ml) bowl. Blend with a fork.
6. Add 1 tablespoon (15 ml) hot starch mixture to egg yolk; blend thoroughly. Repeat 3 more times.
7. Pour egg-starch mixture into remaining starch paste. Blend thoroughly. Observe shiny appearance due to raw egg.
8. Place saucepan over medium heat; stir constantly and heat egg-starch mixture for 3 to 4 minutes or until mixture loses its glossy appearance. Do *not* let mixture boil. Stir in butter or margarine and vanilla; stir until mixture is well blended.
9. Pour into serving dishes.
10. Recipe yields 2 servings of pudding or filling for one 6-inch (15 cm) pie.
11. Record total working time:_____minutes.

Variations

1. **Coconut Cream:** Gently fold in 2 tablespoons (30 ml) flaked or finely chopped coconut before serving.
2. **Banana Cream:** Use 1/2 of cooled pudding for bottom layer. Slice 1/4 ripe banana onto pudding in each serving dish or 1/2 banana over layer of pudding in baked pastry crust. Top with remaining cooled pudding.
3. **Pineapple Cream:** Gently fold in 1/4 cup (50 ml) *thoroughly drained* crushed pineapple before serving.
4. **Nut or Date Cream:** Gently fold in 2 tablespoons (30 ml) chopped nuts or chopped dates before serving.

Cream Pie (See page 134.)

Creamy Tapioca Pudding

Milk	1 cup	250 ml
Tapioca	1 1/2 tablespoons	25 ml
Sugar	2 1/2 tablespoons	40 ml
Salt	few grains	few grains
Egg, separated	1	1
Vanilla	1/2 teaspoon	2 ml

1. Set out three smallest size custard cups.
2. Combine milk, tapioca, 1 tablespoon (15 ml) sugar, salt and egg yolk in a 1–1 1/2 quart (1–1.5 L) saucepan. Allow mixture to stand at least 5 minutes.
3. In a 2 or 3 cup (500 or 750 ml) bowl beat egg white to foamy stage.
4. Add sugar in not less than 4 portions, beating after each addition of sugar. Egg white-sugar meringue should be beaten to stiff peak stage.
5. Place saucepan over medium heat. With constant stirring bring mixture to boil. Remove from heat. Stir in vanilla.
6. Put meringue mixture onto cooked tapioca. Gently fold meringue with tapioca. Do *not* overblend.
7. Pour into serving dishes. Cool.
8. Record total working time: _____ minutes.

CHARACTERISTICS OF HIGH QUALITY STARCH-EGG PRODUCTS

Appearance: Puddings or cooked fruit salad dressing have shiny surface. Film forms on top as cooked mixture cools.

Consistency: Puddings will "mound" on serving spoon or as a pie filling be firm enough to retain a firm, clear-cut edge. Smooth.

Flavor:
  Creamy Cornstarch Pudding: Sweet with *slight* vanilla flavor.
  Creamy Tapioca Pudding: Sweet with *slight* egg and *slight* vanilla flavor.
  Lemon Pudding: Tart lemon.
*Fruit Salad Dressing: Well balanced fruit flavor; tart.

*See page 213 for Fruit Salad Dressing recipe.

REVIEW QUESTIONS

1. What special considerations arise when starch and egg are to be combined in a single food product?
2. Discuss the need for close temperature control in preparing the fruit salad dressing.
3. What variations could be made starting with cream pudding?
4. Discuss role of acid in starch-egg cookery.

Meat–Tender Cuts: Dry Heat Methods

OBJECTIVES

1. To illustrate dry heat methods of cooking tender cuts of meat.
2. To discuss and illustrate factors that determine the tenderness of a cut of meat before cooking.
3. To discuss the effect of cooking on the quality characteristics of the cooked meat.
4. To discuss characteristic differences in fat, bone, muscle color, and texture in meat cuts from different animals.
5. To acquaint the student with selected variety cuts included as *tender* cuts of meat.
6. To acquaint the student with poultry classified as *tender* and to discuss typical quality characteristics of tender birds.

PRODUCTS TO BE PREPARED TO ILLUSTRATE PRINCIPLES

Hamburger patties
Liver (baby beef or calf)
Chicken breasts
Bacon
Pork Chop Suey

PRINCIPLES

1. Tender cuts of meat contain small amounts of collagenous connective tissue as a result of less exercise of the muscle area. In poultry, age of the bird is also a factor.
2. The degree of hydrolysis of collagen will be dependent on the cooking time and temperature.
3. Muscle fiber protein becomes tough with extended application of heat.
4. Some less tender muscles are tenderized by mechanical treatment of grinding. Such ground meat can then be considered and used as a "tender" cut.
5. Bone structure of a young animal or bird is:
   a. Porous since calcification is not completed.
   b. Reddish: blood cells carry nutrients into the bone structure and are trapped in the bone at the time of slaughter.
   c. In poultry the degree of calcification of the keel bone is an indication of the age of the bird.
6. Age of the animal or bird influences the:
   a. Amount of fat deposited.
   b. Color of the fat.
   c. Firmness of the fat.

7. Firmness of the fat is related to the chemical composition (fatty acids) of the fat as determined by:
   a. Inherent animal characteristics.
   b. The diet of the animal.
8. Flavor of muscle fiber protein of both animals and birds is influenced by:
   a. Age.
   b. Amount of exercise of muscle.
   c. Degree of marbling.
   d. Feed.
9. Diameter of the muscle fiber and the size and number of muscle fibers forming the fasciculi determine the texture of meat.
10. Color of muscle fiber protein is an inherent characteristic of the species of animal or fish, but will also relate to the amount of exercise of the specific muscle. This condition is especially noticeable in poultry.

DIRECTIONS FOR DRY HEAT METHODS

Broiling
Meat is directly exposed to the source of heat.
1. If pieces of meat are very lean, the broiler rack should be lightly greased to make it easier to clean.
2. Place cuts of meat on the broiler rack.
3. Place rack under the broiler so the cut surface of the meat is approximately 4 inches (10 cm) from the source of heat. Distance from the source of heat depends on thickness of the cut—*thicker cuts are placed further away.*
4. Cook the meat for approximately half of the total cooking time before turning. The total cooking time will depend on:
   a. Thickness of the cut.
   b. Degree of coagulation desired—rare, medium, or well done for beef. Most other cuts are cooked well done.
5. Salt meat lightly; serve on a well-heated plate or platter.

Pan-Broiling
Heavy metal of frying pan transfer heat to meat.
1. Lightly grease a heavy metal frying pan. Heat, but do not allow the fat to smoke.
2. Meat may be browned by cooking at a higher temperature for about 2 minutes on each side of the piece of meat. Heat may then be reduced until meat has reached desired stage of doneness. See Step 4 in directions for **broiling.**
3. Fat should be removed from the frying pan as it accumulates. Put these drippings in a small glass custard cup.
4. Salt the meat lightly (exception—ham slices and sausage); serve on a well-heated plate or platter.

Pan-Frying
Heavy metal of frying pan transfers heat to meat and to a thin layer of fat in the frying pan.
1. Pan frying differs from pan broiling primarily in the amount of fat used in the frying pan. For pan broiling all excess fat is removed during the cooking period. For pan frying a small amount of fat is kept in the frying pan during the entire cooking period.
2. Where cuts of meat have been coated with flour, as in the case with some chicken and fish cuts, pan frying is more practical than pan broiling, so the coating does not stick to the frying pan.

Stir-Frying (Flash Cooking)

WOK or frying pan transfers heat to a small quantity of oil and to the food (meat and/or vegetables).
1. More fat is used here than in pan frying; vegetable oil is traditionally used.
2. All food must be cleaned and cut into proper shape before the cooking is started. All pieces are small or thinly sliced in order to cook quickly.

Deep-fat Frying

Heat is transferred to the meat through the medium of heated fat or oil. Relatively large amounts of fat or oil are used. The food product may be breaded before frying.

Roasting (Baking)

Meat is in an *uncovered* pan; meat is heated by heated air.
1. Meat is placed on a rack in the baking pan with the fat side up.
2. A meat thermometer will give the most accurate means of determining degree of "doneness" for the cooked piece of meat. The bulb of the meat thermometer should be inserted in the center of the largest muscle of the roast.

PREPARATION OF FRESH MEAT AND POULTRY FOR COOKING

Steaks, Chops, and Roasts

1. Small pieces of bone may adhere to the cut surface of the meat. Gently scrape the cut surface with a knife to remove the loose pieces of bone. Wipe each piece of meat with a damp cloth.
2. Steaks and chops usually have a layer of fat on the exterior side of the piece of meat. Cut through this fat layer *to* the muscle, but do *not* cut into the muscle. Make these cuts about 1 inch apart. This is termed *scoring* the cut. This is done to reduce curling of the cut during cooking.
3. *Do not* salt the meat before cooking because salt draws juices from the muscle fibers through the process of osmosis.

Poultry

1. Trim off inedible portions from either the skin side or the interior wall.
2. Wash entire piece under cold, running tap water.
3. Dry each piece of chicken with paper toweling before cooking.

Pan-Broiled Bacon (See page 254 for Microwave Method.)

Bacon — 2 slices

1. Place bacon strip in a *cold* frying pan. Heat pan slowly so the bacon will not curl. Broil until crisp but not brittle. Turn as needed during the cooking period.
2. Remove bacon to paper towel to drain off excess fat.
3. Use bacon dripping for pan broiling liver.
4. Record total working time:_____minutes.

CHARACTERISTICS OF HIGH QUALITY BACON

Appearance: Slices lie flat on plate; are evenly browned.
Tenderness: Crisp-tender when bitten.
Flavor: Slightly salty; slightly sweet; slightly smoky.

Pan-Broiled Liver

Baby beef or calf liver	4 to 5 ounces	120 to 150 g
*Shortening	1 teaspoon	5 ml
Flour	2 tablespoons	30 ml
Salt	1/4 teaspoon	1 ml
Pepper	few grains	few grains

1. Prepare bacon or onion first if either is to be served with the liver.
2. Remove any outer membrane which may be on the slice of liver; snip out veins with scissors.
3. Blend salt and pepper with flour. Have the flour mixture on a piece of waxed paper or on a flat plate.
4. Dip the liver in the flour mixture. Coat liver on each side. Do not have an excess of flour clinging to the meat.
5. Melt fat in heavy frying pan. Have fat hot but *not* smoking.
6. Brown liver on each side.
7. *Do not overcook.* A total of 5 minutes cooking time may be enough.
8. Liver should be cooked only long enough to bring about a color change in the interior of the meat.
9. Record total working time:＿＿＿＿＿minutes.

*Fat may be derived by broiling one slice of bacon in the frying pan in which the liver is to be cooked.

Sauteed Onion (Can be included in Vegetable Cookery, page 179. Make 3 times recipe.)

Onion, thin slices	2 or 3	2 or 3
Shortening, margarine or butter for flavor	1 tablespoon	15 ml

1. Place shortening in a heavy frying pan. Heat until fat is melted.
2. Add onion slices. Heat slowly until the onion is tender, (approximately 10 minutes.)
3. Remove onion to plate. Add more fat if necessary to pan broil liver.
4. Record total working time:＿＿＿＿＿minutes.

Fried Chicken Breasts

Whole chicken breasts	2	2
Butter or margarine	1 tablespoon	15 ml
Flour	1/4 cup	50 ml
Salt	1/2 teaspoon	2 ml
Pepper (optional)	few grains	few grains

1. Trim and clean chicken breasts as necessary. Rinse in clear water. Drain on paper towels. Cut each breast in half to give 4 pieces. Bone if desired.
2. Blend flour with seasonings on flat dinner plate, on waxed paper, or in a paper bag.
3. Coat each piece of chicken with the seasoned flour. Lightly shake off excess flour.
4. Melt fat in a heavy frying pan. Heat electric frying pan to 350°F (175°C). Fat should be hot but not smoking as the pieces of chicken are added.
5. Brown each piece of chicken. Fat should never be so hot as to smoke.
6. Reduce heat and continue to cook in fat for approximately 25 minutes or more—depending on thickness of the chicken breasts. Fillets cook in shorter time.
7. Record total working time:＿＿＿＿＿minutes.

Pan-Broiled Ground Beef Patties (See page 254 for Microwave Method.)

*Ground beef or hamburger	4 ounces	120 g
Shortening	1/2–1 teaspoon	2–5 ml

1. Shape the ground meat into one patty 3/4–1 inch (2–2.5 cm) thick.
2. Melt the shortening in a heavy fry pan. Use only enough fat to prevent sticking. The fat should be hot, but not smoking.
3. Place the patty on the greased portion of the fry pan. Cook the patty 4 to 5 minutes on each side depending on thickness of the patty.
4. If hamburger is used and is quite fat, remove excess fat from fry pan as the patty cooks. Fat should not be allowed to accumulate in the fry pan.
5. The patty can be turned more than once during cooking. However, *do not* press patty against dry pan with spatula or turner; this presses juices out of the patty, resulting in a dry product.
6. Ground beef patties should be cooked to the well-done stage.
7. The ground beef patties will be evaluated without added salt and pepper. However, in the normal preparation, seasonings would be added at this time.
8. Record total working time:_____minutes.

*Ground beef or hamburger with textured vegetable protein may be used here.

Stir-Fry Pork Chop Suey

Oil	2 tablespoons	30 ml
Pork, fresh, shreds	1/4–1 cup	50–250 ml
Chinese cabbage, shredded	1/2 cup	125 ml
Celery, 1/2 inch rounds	1/4 cup	50 ml
Green pepper, shredded	1	1
Green onions, minced	3	3
Bean sprouts, rinsed	1/2 cup	125 ml
Beef stock (or chicken)	1 cup	250 ml
Salt (optional)	1/2 teaspoon	2 ml
Soy sauce	2 tablespoons	30 ml
Cornstarch	1 tablespoon	15 ml
Water, cold	3 tablespoons	45 ml

1. Prepare ingredients; mix cornstarch and water.
2. Set ingredients by the WOK in the order listed.
3. Set the WOK thermostat on high (400°F) for 30 seconds, add the oil and count to 30.
4. Add pork shreds and stir-fry 30 seconds.
5. Add the vegetables at 30 second intervals, stir-frying continuously. After bean sprouts have been added, continue to stir-fry for 3 minutes.
6. Push the ingredients to the sides of the WOK.
7. Pour beef stock down the side of the WOK; add soy sauce and salt; stir.
8. Add the cornstarch-water mixture; stir until the cornstarch gelatinizes and becomes clear.
9. Mix with solid ingredients; serve immediately in a heated dish.
10. Record total working time:_____minutes.

Note: This recipe may be stir-fried in an electric fry pan (Teflon® coated) if a WOK is not available.
Rice may be served with this recipe; see page 100.

Pan-Baked Chicken Breasts

Whole chicken breasts	2	2
Butter or margarine	1 tablespoon	15 ml
Flour	1/4 cup	50 ml
Salt	1/2 teaspoon	2 ml
Pepper (optional)	few grains	few grains

1. Preheat oven to 425°F (200°C).
2. Trim chicken breasts as necessary. Wash in clear water. Dry with paper towels. Cut each breast in half to give 4 pieces. Bone if desired.
3. Blend flour with seasonings.
4. Melt butter in pan in which the chicken is to be baked. Dip each piece of chicken in the melted fat. Arrange in the baking pan with the skin side up. Carefully dredge (dust) each piece of chicken with the flour mixture.
5. Bake uncovered in an oven preheated to 425°F (200°C) for 45–60 minutes. Baste with the fat in the pan twice during the baking period. Do this quickly. Do not allow oven to cool off while basting. Fillets will bake in shorter time.
6. Record total working time:_____minutes.

CHARACTERISTICS OF HIGH QUALITY MEAT AND POULTRY

Appearance: All cooked meat is opaque and moist. Color of cooked meat—*outside:* rich brown; *interior:* beef, from deep red or pink (rare meat) through a light pink (medium) to a light gray or brown (well done); pork, from almost white to light gray with certain muscles being light brown; veal, predominately light gray. Color of cooked poultry varies from a creamy white in light meat to a light to medium brown in dark meat.
Texture: Determined by the diameter of the muscle fibers and the diameter of the fasciculi; cuts having fibers and fasciculi of small diameter are fine grained while cuts having fibers and fasciculi of large diameter are coarse grained (see Texture of Meat below).
Tenderness: Some resistance to chewing, but sample should be easily masticated.
Juiciness: Free-flowing juice in cuts cooked to rare stage changing to noticeable moistness in cuts cooked to the well-done stage.
Flavor: Typical for cut of meat; meat flavor characteristic of breed should predominate.

TEXTURE OF MEAT

Fine-grain meat: Cuts from rib and loin of beef, pork and lamb; veal; white meat of broilers.
Medium-fine-grain meat: Top round steak; ham.
Medium-coarse-grain meat: Bottom round steak; blade and arm steaks of beef; dark meat of poultry.
Coarse-grain meat: Flank steak, stewing hen; duck.

Note: Ground meat is usually coarse. Texture of ground meat is determined by the diameter of the holes in the grinder plate and the number of times the meat is put through the grinder rather than by the diameter of the fibers and fasciculi.

EVALUATION OF PRODUCTS
(MEAT)

Name: _____

Date: _____

Score System

Points	Quality
7	Excellent
6	Very good
5	Good
4	Medium
3	Fair
2	Poor
1	Very poor

Directions:

1. Place the numerical score in the box in the upper left hand corner.
2. Comments should justify the numerical score. Comments must be brief.
3. Evaluation of the food products must be on an *individual* basis.

Products

Quality Characteristic					
Outside Appearance					
Interior Appearance					
Tenderness					
Juiciness					
Flavor					

143

Meat—Less Tender Cuts: Moist Heat Methods

OBJECTIVES

1. To illustrate moist heat methods of cooking less tender cuts of meat.
2. To review the factors that cause a cut of meat to be considered "less tender."
3. To illustrate that collagenous tissue will hydrolyze in the presence of heat and moisture.
4. To illustrate principles applied in the breading of a meat, fish, or poultry product.
5. To illustrate the effectiveness of the mechanical treatment of pounding to break down collagenous connective tissue.
6. To acquaint the student with selected variety meats considered less tender meats.
7. To acquaint the student with the principles and the use of the pressure saucepan.

PRODUCTS TO BE PREPARED TO ILLUSTRATE PRINCIPLES

Swiss steak
Breaded veal chop
Braised pork chop
Braised chicken thighs
Spiced tongue
Veal rosemary (optional)
Lamb stew (optional)
Lamb curry (optional)

PRINCIPLES

1. Hydrolysis of collagen is a function of:
   a. Temperature—time.
   b. Pressure.
   c. Addition of acid.
2. Both collagen and elastin can be broken down by mechanical means to increase the tenderness of the cut of meat.
   a. Pounding or "Swissing."
   b. Grinding.
3. Muscle fiber protein is toughened by excessive heat.
4. Cooking losses increase with an increase in temperature and pressure.
5. Breading may be used as a means of retaining moisture.

Braised Pork Chops

Pork rib or pork loin chop   1

1. Score fat on the outside of the chop.
2. Preheat heavy frying pan (#5 for class use).
3. Grease the bottom of the frying pan by holding the fat side of the chop against the bottom of the warm frying pan. Rub fat over area to be covered by the chop.
4. Place chop flat on the frying pan. Brown on each side. *Do not* have frying pan too hot. Fat should *not* smoke.
5. Add approximately 2 tablespoons (30 ml) water to the browned chop. Cover frying pan with a tight-fitting lid. Cook at simmering temperature about 30 minutes. Cook longer if necessary—until the chop is tender.
6. Do not let the meat cook dry. Add a small amount of moisture, if necessary. (Melted fat may give the appearance of liquid during cooking when actually no water may be present.)
7. A tablespoon (15 ml) of water may be added to the drippings to give a pan gravy to serve over the chop.
8. Record total working time:_____ minutes.

*Chicken Thighs

Chicken thighs	3 or 4	3 or 4
Flour	1/4 cup	50 ml
Salt	1/2 teaspoon	2 ml
Pepper (optional)	few grains	few grains
Butter or margarine	2 tablespoons	30 ml

1. Trim and clean chicken thighs as necessary. Rinse in clear water. Drain and dry with paper toweling.
2. Blend together the flour, salt, and pepper. Place on a flat plate, on waxed paper, or in a paper bag.
3. Coat the chicken thighs with flour. Lightly shake off excess flour.
*4. Melt fat in a pressure saucepan. Fat should not be so hot that it separates or smokes.
5. Add the floured chicken thighs: brown to deep golden brown on both sides.
6. Remove thighs from pressure saucepan: insert rack and place thighs on rack.
7. Add 1 cup (250 ml) of water or enough water to have water the depth of the rack. Pieces of chicken should not lie in water.
8. Position cover on pressure saucepan: heat until steam flows in a steady stream through lid vent for 2 minutes.
9. Position pressure gauge on vent: count cooking time from the time the gauge registers 10 pounds pressure. Regulate heat controls to keep pressure constant for the 15-minute cooking period.
10. Place the pressure saucepan under cold running water for 2 minutes. *Do not* let water run over the pressure gauge. When pressure is at 0, remove the pressure gauge and then the lid. *Use caution* in removing the lid (use lid as a screen between you and any steam that may still be in the saucepan).
11. Gravy may be made with the drippings: use 2 tablespoons (30 ml) flour for each cup of drippings. (Apply principles of starch cookery.)
12. Record total working time:_____ minutes.

*Chicken thighs could be braised. Use of the pressure saucepan is included here to give students additional experience with this method of cookery.

Breaded Braised Veal Chop or Cutlet

Veal chop or cutlet	1	1
Egg	1	1
Water	2 tablespoons	30 ml
Crumbs, fine, sifted	1/4 cup	50 ml
Shortening	1 tablespoon	15 ml
Salt	1/4 teaspoon	1 ml

1. Add the water to the egg. Blend with a fork or beater until yolk and white are just blended—egg should not be foamy. Pour blended egg into a flat dish or plate so the chop or cutlet will lie flat in the egg. Dip the meat in the egg so each side of the meat is covered with egg. (Score outer covering of chop before dipping in egg.)
2. Add the salt to the crumbs. Place the crumbs on a piece of waxed paper. Place the egg-coated meat in the crumbs; turn so both sides become coated with crumbs.
3. If a heavy coating of crumbs is desired, the meat may be dipped in the egg a second time and then in the crumbs again. Usually one coating is sufficient.
4. Melt the fat in a heavy frying pan (#5 for class use). Brown the meat on each side. Do *not* have the fat too hot—the fat should *not* smoke.
5. *Reduce heat;* add about 1 tablespoon (15 ml) of water; cover frying pan with a tight-fitting cover. Simmer for 3/4 to 1 hour or until meat is tender.
6. It may be necessary to add additional water during the cooking period.
7. Record total working time:_____ minutes.

Swiss Steak

Round steak	4–5 ounces	120–150 g
Flour	2 tablespoons	30 ml
Salt	1/4 teaspoon	1 ml
Pepper	few grains	few grains
Shortening	1 tablespoon	15 ml
Onion slices (1/4 inch or 4 cm thick)	2–3	2–3
Canned tomatoes, tomato juice or hot water	1/2 cup	125 ml

1. Steak would usually be cut approximately 1 1/2 inches (3.8 cm) thick. For class work it will be approximately 1 inch (2.5 cm) thick to speed cooking time.
2. Blend together the flour and seasonings. Put the flour onto a sheet of waxed paper large enough to hold the meat. Rub the flour into each side of the meat. Then pound meat with the side of a plate or with a Swissing iron. Almost all of the flour should be held by the meat by the time the meat is pounded. Turn meat during pounding so flour is distributed on each side of the meat.
3. Melt fat in a heavy (#5 for class) frying pan; have fat hot, but *not* smoking. Add meat and brown meat on each side.
4. Add tomatoes and onion slices; cover with a closely fitting lid; simmer until tender. Add more liquid (water or tomato juice) as needed.
5. This may be baked for approximately 1 1/2 hours in a 350°F (175°C) oven. Place in oven after covering—in Step 4.
6. At the end of the cooking period, there should be some thickened sauce on the meat.
7. Record total working time:_____ minutes.

Spiced Veal Tongue

Veal tongue	1	1
*Water	1 cup	250 ml
Salt	1 teaspoon	5 ml
Celery	1 stalk	1 stalk
Onions, small, sliced	2	2
Cloves, whole	6	6
Bay leaf	1	1
Peppercorns, whole	6	6
Cornstarch	2 tablespoons	30 ml
Brown sugar	1/2 cup	125 ml
Vinegar	1/4 cup	50 ml

1. Remove dry skin from onions; wash, dry and slice into 1/4-inch (4 mm) thick slices. Wash and dry celery stalk; cut into 1-inch (2.5 cm) thick slices.
†2. Rinse tongue under cold tap water. Place tongue, water, salt, celery, cloves, bay leaf, peppercorns and onions in a pressure saucepan.** Cover saucepan; heat until a steady stream of steam is produced. Place pressure gauge on steam vent; allow pressure to reach 15 pounds. Cook for 30 minutes at 15 pounds pressure.
3. At the end of the cooking period, stand covered saucepan under cold running water until the pan feels cool. Remove pressure gauge and open saucepan.
4. Remove skin from tongue and slice meat into 1/4-inch (6 mm) thick slices.
5. Strain meat broth. Blend cornstarch with brown sugar and vinegar. Add this mixture to 1 cup (250 ml) of the strained meat broth and bring to a boil.
6. Reduce heat to a simmer and add meat slices. Simmer meat in sauce for 5 minutes.
7. Serve meat slices with a small amount of the sauce.
8. Record total working time:_____minutes.

*Water should just cover rack on bottom of pressure saucepan.

**A pressure saucepan is used for this product to reduce the cooking time so the product can be prepared in a two-hour laboratory period.

†The rack should be in place in the bottom of the pressure saucepan before food is added.

Braised Veal Rosemary

Veal round or veal cutlet	1 pound	450	g
Flour	1/4 cup	50	ml
Salt	1 teaspoon	5	ml
Pepper	1/8 teaspoon	0.5	ml
Paprika	2 teaspoons	10	ml
Shortening	3 tablespoons	45	ml
Onions, medium, sliced	2	2	
Rosemary	1/4 teaspoon	1	ml
Water	1/3 cup	75	ml
Sour cream	3/4 cup	175	ml

1. Blend flour with all of seasonings except rosemary.
2. Cut veal into bite-size pieces. Rub each piece with seasoned flour.
3. Melt 2 tablespoons (30 ml) of the fat in a heavy frying pan; add pieces of veal and brown the veal on each side.
4. Remove dry skin from onions; wash; slice into 1/4-inch (6 mm) thick slices. In a separate, small frying pan melt the remaining fat; add onion slices; cook onions slowly until lightly golden in color.
5. Arrange the meat so each piece can be sprinkled with a portion of the rosemary; arrange the onion slices over the seasoned pieces of veal.
6. Add water. Tightly cover the frying pan. Simmer slowly for about 1 hour or until the veal is tender. (Do not over brown the meat; do *not* let the meat scorch during the final cooking period). Remove meat to a warm serving plate.
7. Blend sour cream with liquid in the pan just before serving; do not boil sour cream; pour over meat.
8. Record total working time:_____minutes.

Lamb Curry

Boneless lamb shoulder	1 pound	450 g
Salt	1 teaspoon	5 ml
Garlic clove, small	1	1
Onion, large	1	1
Celery, diced	1 cup	250 ml
Curry powder	1/2–1 teaspoon	2–5 ml
Apple, tart, medium	1	1
Rice, long grain, converted	2/3 cup	150 ml

1. Cut the meat into 1-inch (2.5 cm) cubes (can be smaller for class use to reduce cooking time). Trim away excess fat while cubing the meat.
2. Place the cubed lamb in a saucepan; barely cover with water and add salt; cover saucepan and simmer approximately 1 hour.
3. Place the fat trimmed from the meat in an electric frying pan; heat slowly to fry out the fat; remove tissue left after the fat has been melted.
4. Remove dry skin from onions; wash, dry and slice into 1/4-inch (6 mm) thick slices. Wash (trim if necessary) and dry celery stalk; dice into 1/4-inch (6 mm) dice. Remove dry skin from garlic clove; wash, dry and impale with a toothpick. Add these vegetables to the hot fat; cook for 5 minutes; remove garlic clove.
5. While the onion-celery mixture is cooking, wash, pare, core, and finely chop the apple. Add to the onion-celery mixture; add the curry powder (add the smaller amount first—then add as desired). Add the lamb with whatever liquid remains on the lamb. Simmer uncovered for approximately 20 minutes. (Mixture can be covered if no excess water is on the lamb.)
6. Serve over cooked rice. (See page 100 for cooking of rice.)
7. Record total working time:_____ minutes.

Lamb Stew

Boneless lamb shoulder	1 pound	450	g
Flour	1/4 cup	50	ml
Salt	1 teaspoon	5	ml
Pepper	1/8 teaspoon	0.5	ml
Shortening	2 tablespoons	30	ml
Water, boiling	3 cups	750	ml
Onions, small	6	6	
Carrots, medium large	2	2	
Potatoes, medium large	2	2	
Peas, frozen, thawed	1 cup	250	ml
Parsley, minced	1 tablespoon	15	ml

1. Blend the flour, salt, and pepper. Cut the lamb into approximately 1-inch (2.5 cm) cubes. Place flour on a plate or waxed paper. Roll each piece of lamb in flour mixture. Shake off excess flour. (Save excess flour to thicken gravy later, if needed. See Step 7.)
*2. Melt fat in the bottom of a pressure saucepan; have fat hot, but *not* smoking. Add lamb pieces; brown on all sides.
3. Add 1 cup (250 ml) boiling water to meat; lock pressure saucepan cover in place; heat until a steady stream of steam comes through the vent; place pressure gauge over vent. Cook at 10 pounds pressure for 30 minutes.
4. Remove dry skins from onions; wash. Use vegetable peeler to pare carrots and potatoes; wash. Cut carrots into 1-inch (2.5 cm) lengths; cut each potato into 6–8 pieces. To the remaining 2 cups (500 ml) of boiling water, add the whole onions and the carrots; boil (with saucepan partially covered) for 10 minutes; add potatoes and boil an additional 10 minutes or until vegetables are *barely* tender. *Do not overcook* the vegetables. Have vegetables cooked by the time the stew meat is ready. Save cooking liquid to add to meat, if desired.
5. At the end of the 30-minute cooking period, hold the pressure saucepan under a stream of cold tap water to reduce the pressure (2 minutes under cold running water). Remove pressure gauge and then remove lid.
6. Carefully transfer the cooked vegetables to the meat; add frozen peas; add liquid from vegetables if additional liquid is necessary; heat meat and vegetables for about 5 minutes or until peas are cooked.
7. If liquid needs to be thickened, blend 2 tablespoons (30 ml) of flour (use seasoned flour remaining from Step 1) with 1/2 cup (125 ml) cold water. Add a portion of the hot liquid to the starch paste and then add all the flour mixture to the stew. This mixture must be brought to a boil to cook the starch. *Do not overstir* the stew mixture during the final stages of preparation.
8. Garnish with minced parsley. Wash and thoroughly drain parsley before mincing.
9. Record total working time:_____ minutes.

*Insert rack before proceeding to next step.

EVALUATION OF PRODUCTS
(MEAT)

Name: _____

Date: _____

Score System

Points	Quality
7	Excellent
6	Very good
5	Good
4	Medium
3	Fair
2	Poor
1	Very poor

Directions:

1. Place the numerical score in the box in the upper left hand corner.
2. Comments should justify the numerical score. Comments must be brief.
3. Evaluation of the food products must be on an *individual* basis.

Products

Quality Characteristic					
Outside Appearance					
Interior Appearance					
Tenderness					
Juiciness					
Flavor					

153

REVIEW QUESTIONS

1. List and explain the factors considered in the grading of meat.
2. a. What does the federal inspection of meat and poultry indicate to the consumer?
   b. Is meat shipped interstate required to be federally inspected?
   c. How does the law effect meat that is not shipped in interstate trade?
3. a. Define rigor mortis.
   b. What role does rigor mortis play in the tenderness of cooked meat?
4. a. What effect does aging (ripening) have on the quality characteristics of meat?
   b. What types of meat are normally given a ripening period?
5. How can bone and fat be used to indicate the age of an animal or a bird?
6. a. Name three proteins found in muscle fibers.
   b. Name the two proteins that constitute the connective tissue.
   c. What happens to each of the five proteins [in (a) and (b)] when they are heated during the cooking process?
7. Briefly discuss the relationships between the amount of connective tissue in a piece of meat and the proper cooking method for the piece of meat.
8. It is recommended that small, tender cuts of pork and veal not be cooked by dry heat. What method is recommended? Give reasons.
9. Hamburger frequently is prepared from one of the less tender cuts of beef, yet it is frequently pan broiled or broiled. Why?
10. a. What factors determine the texture of meat?
    b. Name some retail cuts of meat that have a fine texture.
    c. Name some retail cuts of meat that have a coarse texture.
11. Why are "time per pound" tables only an approximation rather than a definite guide to degree of doneness?
12. Discuss the relationship of oven temperature during roasting (baking) to the tenderness and juiciness of the finished roast.
13. Discuss the relationship of internal temperature to which a roast is cooked to tenderness and juiciness.
14. What is the function(s) of each of the following ingredients in the preparation of the product indicated?
    a. Tomato in Swiss steak.
    b. Egg on veal chop.
    c. Bread crumbs on veal chop.
15. a. Why does the use of a pressure saucepan reduce the cooking time?
    b. List the important steps to consider to insure the *safe* use of a pressure saucepan.
16. List and discuss factors which will affect the flavor of meat and poultry.
17. In poultry, how does the amount of exercise of the specific muscle relate to:
    a. Color of the muscle?
    b. Tenderness of the muscle?
    c. Texture of the muscle?
    d. Flavor of the muscle?
18. a. List the various classifications of poultry and indicate the proper cooking procedure for each class of bird.
    b. Explain why some types are normally cooked by dry heat methods of cooking.
19. a. Compare the nutritive value of meat and poultry.
    b. What is the relationship between method of preparation and nutritive value?

20. The products listed in the table were evaluated as indicated. What was done to these products to account for such an evaluation?

Quality Characteristic	Ground Beef Patty	Chicken Thigh	Veal Tongue
Outside Appearance	5 Well browned	3 Overbrowned	3 Sauce too thin
Interior	3 Red	3 Stringy	5
Tenderness	5	5	6
Juiciness	5	4 Interior dry	5
Flavor	3 Raw	4 Lacks flavor	3 Too tart

Fish and Shellfish

OBJECTIVES

1. To illustrate factors to be considered in the selection of fish and shellfish.
2. To illustrate different types of fish and shellfish.
3. To illustrate different market forms (cuts) of fish.
4. To demonstrate factors affecting the cooking of several types of fish and shellfish.

PRODUCTS TO BE PREPARED TO ILLUSTRATE PRINCIPLES

Shrimp
Pan-fried perch
Broiled salmon steaks
Whole baked fish
Oven-poached finnan haddie
"Oven-fried" fillets (optional)
Baked scallops (optional)

PRINCIPLES

1. Biology
   a. The chemistry of living organisms is geared to the environment in which the organisms exists.
   b. The bodily processes are regulated by enzymes, which in fish function at lower temperatures than the enzyme systems of mammals such as cows, hogs, or sheep.
   c. An increase of temperature causes the enzyme systems to function more rapidly, which in the case of fish and shellfish has important practical considerations for storage and handling.
2. Storage
   a. Storage of fish and shellfish at higher than refrigeration temperature, 42°-50°F (6°-10°C), will cause rapid deterioration of the flesh, rendering the flesh inedible.
   b. Even at low temperatures, fish and shellfish can be stored for only a short time.
   c. Prolonged storage requires some method of preservation such as freezing, canning, brining, smoking, or a combination of these methods.
   d. Fish and shellfish should be kept tightly covered or wrapped when stored because of their distinctive odors, which are readily absorbed by other foods.

3. Cookery
   a. Fish and shellfish contain little connective tissue so they can be cooked by any method of cookery.
   b. Because most fish contain small amounts of fat, some fat is generally added during the cooking process.
   c. Dry heat methods of cookery are usually preferred; dry heat methods develop more flavor.
   d. Fish to be cooked by moist-heat methods of cookery is frequently wrapped in parchment or cheesecloth to hold the flesh together as the fish cooks.
   e. As purchased, fish and shellfish usually require washing and some cleaning before being cooked.
   f. Shrimp, especially, should be washed, peeled, deveined, and rinsed before cooking.
   g. Fish and shellfish must be cooked to the well-done stage to be palatable and to be bacteriologically safe.
   h. Fish flesh is sufficiently cooked when the flesh separates easily into flakes.
   i. Overcooked fish and shellfish are tough and rubbery.
   j. High cooking temperatures and long cooking times are generally to be avoided.
   k. Smoked fish, dried fish, and salted fish may be soaked in water prior to cooking to:
      (1) Rehydrate muscle tissue.
      (2) Reduce smoke flavor in cooked fish.
      (3) Reduce salt flavor in cooked fish.

Shrimp

Shrimp, fresh or frozen, thawed in the shell
  (Number to cook, will be assigned)

1. Peel off the shell of fresh or frozen, thawed shrimp.
2. With a sharp knife, cut along the outside of the center back only deep enough to expose the sand vein. (This is the intestinal tract.)
3. Remove the sand vein, which may vary in color from light tan to black depending on contents.
4. Wash the shrimp in running, cold tap water. Hold in cold tap water until it is ready to cook.
5. Add 3/4 teaspoon (3 ml) salt to each cup of water used for cooking shrimp.
6. Bring the water to a boil.
7. Add the cleaned shrimp to the boiling water. *Reduce heat.*
*8. Cook at simmering temperature, 185°–200°F, (85°–90°C), for 5 minutes or until the meat becomes opaque and some portions of the outer surface become light coral pink.
9. Drain. Put the shrimp into ice water to chill if they are to be served cold. *Do not serve in cocktail sauce* for class evaluation.
10. Record total working time: _____ minutes.

   *To determine the effect of overcooking, leave one or two of the shrimp in the cooking water and boil, 212°F (100°C), these shrimp for 10 minutes. Observe the shrinkage during the cooking period. Compare with the simmered shrimp for *tenderness.*

CHARACTERISTICS OF HIGH QUALITY COOKED SHRIMP

   Appearance: Opaque white with salmon colored (pink-orange) striations.
   Texture: Firm; (does not flake).
   Juiciness: Slightly moist to very slightly dry.
   Tenderness: Very slight resistance to chewing.
   Flavor: Very mild, typical; should not have any fishy flavor.

Pan-Fried Ocean Perch

Perch fillets	2	2
Milk	2 tablespoons	30 ml
Salt	1/4 teaspoon	1 ml
Flour	2 tablespoons	30 ml
Pepper (optional)	few grains	few grains
Shortening or butter or margarine	1 tablespoon	15 ml

1. Blend seasonings with the flour. Place on a piece of waxed paper.
2. Dip perch fillet in milk and then in seasoned flour.
3. Melt fat in heavy frying pan; do *not* overheat, especially if butter or margarine is used. Add flour-coated perch fillets. Fry until fillets are golden brown on each side; the flesh will tend to flake.
4. Serve with Tartar Sauce, page 163.
5. Record total working time: _____ minutes.

*Broiled Salmon Steak

Salmon steak, 3/4-inch (2 cm) thick	1	1
Butter or margarine	1 tablespoon	15 ml
Lemon juice (optional)	1 tablespoon	15 ml
Lemon wedge	1	1

1. Preheat broiler.
2. Arrange salmon steak directly on a broiler pan or on an ovenglass serving platter. (Broiler rack may be lightly greased.)
3. Melt butter or margarine; add lemon juice (if used); spoon half the mixture over surface of steak.
4. Place the broiler pan so the surface of the fish is 3–4 inches (8–10 cm) below the broiler unit. Broil until the surface of the fish is browned—about 10 minutes. If the fish does not appear thoroughly cooked (when the surface is browned), bake in a 350°F (175°C) oven until the fish "flakes".
5. Spoon remaining lemon-butter sauce over fish as it broils or at the end of the cooking period. Do *not* serve in pools of butter.
6. Serve with wedge of lemon.
7. Record total working time: _____minutes.

Note: Other fat-fleshed fish as halibut or swordfish may be broiled.

"Oven-Fried" Fish Fillets or Steaks

Haddock fillets or steaks (Steaks cut 1/2–3/4 inch thick or 1–2 cm)	1 pound	450 g
Half and Half	1/2 cup	125 ml
Salt	3/4 teaspoon	3 ml
Pepper	few grains	few grains
Paprika	1/4 teaspoon	1 ml
Butter or margarine	3 tablespoons	45 ml
Bread crumbs, dry, fine, sifted	1 cup	250 ml

1. Preheat oven to 550°F (290°C).
2. Add the seasonings to the Half and Half.
3. Melt butter or margarine.
4. Mix 1 tablespoon (15 ml) melted butter with the crumbs.
5. Cut fish fillets into serving portions; dip fish portions into Half and Half, then into the crumbs. Have an even coating of crumbs on each portion of fish.
6. Arrange the prepared pieces of fish 2 inches (5 cm) apart in a shallow baking pan. Drizzle the remaining melted butter evenly over the fish.
7. Place the baking pan on the top rack, about 4 inches (10 cm) from the top of the oven, preheated to 550°F (290°C). Bake until the top surface of the fish is well-browned.
8. If the fish is not completely cooked by the time the surface has browned, reduce the oven temperature to 350°F (175°C) and continue baking until the flesh "flakes" easily when tested with a fork. Total cooking time may be 8–12 minutes depending on the thickness of steaks or fillets.
9. Serve with Tartar Sauce, page 163.
10. Record total working time: _____ minutes.

Finnan Haddie Poached in Milk

Finnan Haddie	1/4 pound	110 g
Milk	1 1/2 cups	375 ml
Flour	1 1/2 tablespoons	25 ml

1. Preheat oven to 400°F (200°C).
2. Finnan haddie is smoked haddock. Wash the fish in warm water. It may be desirable to let the fish soak in warm water for 20 minutes before poaching. Change water after 10 minutes for less smoke flavor.
3. Any bones or skin may be removed before placing in baking pan.
4. Select a baking pan deep enough so the fish can be just covered with hot milk as it bakes. Place the fish in the baking dish; add milk to cover. Cover baking dish.
5. *Do not add* salt.
6. Reduce oven setting to 350°F (175°C) when placing fish in oven. Bake for 30 minutes; remove cover; bake about 15 minutes more.
7. Place fish on a serving plate. Strain and measure milk that remains.
8. Prepare white sauce using 1 cup (250 ml) of the strained milk. Cool approximately one quarter of the milk; add the flour; blend until flour is evenly dispersed. Add remaining hot milk. Heat to boiling with constant stirring; boil 1 minute. Serve sauce over finnan haddie. Make sauce quickly so fish does not become cold before serving.
9. Record total working time:_____ minutes.

*Smoked cod may be substituted for finnan haddie.

Baked Scallops

Scallops	4 to 6	4 to 6
Milk	1/4 cup	50 ml
Salt	1/2 teaspoon	2 ml
Flour	1/4 cup	50 ml
Egg	1	1
Water	2 tablespoons	30 ml
Bread crumbs, dry, fine, sifted	1/2 cup	125 ml
Butter or margarine	2 tablespoons	30 ml

1. Preheat oven to 350°F (175°C).
2. Add the salt to the milk. Stir until salt is dissolved.
3. Dip scallops in the seasoned milk.
4. Dip into flour and coat evenly with flour. (Put flour on a piece of waxed paper.)
5. Stir egg until yolk and white are blended. Add the water. Blend. (Egg and water may be blended with a beater, but do not beat until foamy.)
6. Dip the flour-coated scallops into the egg.
7. Place the sifted crumbs on a piece of waxed paper. Place the egg-covered scallops in the crumbs; coat with crumbs.
8. Lightly butter the bottom of a shallow baking dish. Place the crumb-coated scallops in the baking dish.
9. Evenly drizzle the melted fat over the scallops.
10. Bake in a 350°F (175°C) oven until the crumbs are golden brown; the interior of the scallops becomes clear white. Baking time: approximately 30 minutes.
11. Record total working time:_____minutes.

Whole Baked Fish

*White fish, whole	2–3 pounds	1–1.5 kg
Bread cubes, 1/2 inch (1.3 cm) dice, soft	1 quart	1 L
Butter or margarine, melted	1/2 cup	125 ml
Salt	1 teaspoon	5 ml
Pepper	1/8 teaspoon	0.5 ml
Onion, finely chopped	1 tablespoon	15 ml
Parsley, finely chopped	1 tablespoon	15 ml
Pickle relish, sweet	1 tablespoon	15 ml
Butter, melted (additional), for use at Step 7	2 tablespoons	30 ml

1. Preheat oven to 450°F (230°C).
2. Thoroughly wash fish. Remove any scales which may remain on the skin; the head may be removed.
3. Starting at the head end, carefully remove the backbone and rib bones the length of the fish. This makes the serving of the baked fish much easier.
4. Make the dressing from the remaining ingredients. Place the bread cubes in a bowl; Carefully stir in the melted fat with a fork; add other ingredients. *Do not* overstir.
5. Lightly salt the interior of the fish. Arrange the stuffing in the cavity.
6. Hold the sides of the fish together with skewers or heavy toothpicks. Hold skewers in position by lacing with heavy cord.
7. Arrange on an ovenglass baking dish; spoon 1 to 2 tablespoons (15–30 ml) melted butter over the surface of the fish.
8. Reduce oven setting to 350°F (175°C) when placing stuffed fish in oven for baking. Bake in oven for about 1 hour. Fish will easily separate into "flakes" when done.
9. Serve with Drawn Butter Sauce, page 163.
10. Record total working time:_____ minutes.

*Two fillets of 1 pound (450 g) each may be used here. Skewer or sew together loosely 1 side and 2 ends of the fillets; fill cavity with dressing and complete closure.

CHARACTERISTICS OF HIGH QUALITY COOKED FISH

Appearance: Typical for method of cookery; boiled and poached products will not have a browned surface; surface of fish cooked by broiling, baking, or frying will generally have a golden brown surface.
Texture: Fish easily separates into flakes.
Juiciness: Flakes of fish will appear moist.
Tenderness: Some resistance to chewing, but sample should be easily masticated.
Flavor: Typical of variety of fish or seafood but not a distinct fishy flavor or aroma.

Cocktail Sauce

Catsup	2 tablespoons	30 ml
Lemon juice	1 tablespoon	15 ml
Salt	1/4 teaspoon	1 ml
Horseradish (freshly grated for best flavor)	1 teaspoon	5 ml
Worcestershire sauce	1/4 teaspoon	1 ml
Tabasco sauce	1–2 drops	1–2 drops

1. Blend together all ingredients.
2. Chill for best flavor.
3. Serve as accompaniment to cooked shrimp.

Tartar Sauce

Mayonnaise	1/3 cup	75 ml
Sour cucumber pickles, minced	2 teaspoons	10 ml
Green olives, minced	2 teaspoons	10 ml
Capers	1/2 teaspoon	2 ml
Green onion or chives, minced	1/2 teaspoon	2 ml
Parsley, minced	1/2 teaspoon	2 ml
Tarragon vinegar	1/2 teaspoon	2 ml

1. Mix all ingredients together.
2. Serve cold.

Drawn Butter Sauce

Butter or margarine	3 tablespoons	45 ml
Flour	1 1/2 tablespoons	25 ml
Salt	1/4 teaspoon	1 ml
Cayenne	few grains	few grains
Water, boiling	1 cup	250 ml

1. Melt 2 tablespoons (30 ml) of the fat in the upper part of the double boiler.
2. Add the flour; stir until well blended.
3. Add the boiling water gradually; stir until smooth after each addition of water.
4. Bring to a boil over direct heat with continuous stirring.
5. Stir in the remaining butter just before serving. Serve hot.

REVIEW QUESTIONS

1. a. Explain why fish must be stored at refrigerator temperatures.
    b. Compare keeping quality of fish and red meat, both being held at refrigerator temperature.
    c. List some other methods of preservation which can be used to extend the keeping quality of fish.
2. Distinguish between a fish steak and a fish fillet.
3. a. Compare the quantity of connective tissue in a fish with the amount of connective tissue in a chicken breast.
    b. Relate the amount of connective tissue in fish to the methods used in cooking fish.
4. Why is smoked and/or salted fish soaked in fresh cool water before cooking?
5. What principles were violated to account for the evaluations given in the table below?

Quality Characteristic	Shrimp		Poached Cod		Salmon Steak	
Outside Appearance	2	Black stripe down center back	1	Disintegrated	2	Overbrowned
Interior Appearance	5		1	Disintegrated	5	
Tenderness	2	Tough, stringy, rubbery	5		5	
Juiciness	4		2	Dry	5	
Flavor	2	Bitter	5		5	

EVALUATION OF PRODUCTS
(FISH; SEA FOOD)

Name: _____

Date: _____

Directions:

1. Place the numerical score in the box in the upper left hand corner.
2. Comments should justify the numerical score. Comments must be brief.
3. Evaluation of the food products must be on an *individual* basis.

Score System

Points	Quality
7	Excellent
6	Very good
5	Good
4	Medium
3	Fair
2	Poor
1	Very poor

Products

Quality Characteristic					
Outside Appearance					
Interior Appearance					
Tenderness					
Juiciness					
Flavor					

165

Vegetables

OBJECTIVES

1. To study selected vegetables for quality characteristic changes caused by:
   a. Method and time of cooking.
   b. Addition of acid.
   c. Addition of baking soda.
2. To study the relationship between varietal characteristics and quality characteristics for selected varieties of potatoes.
3. To further illustrate principles of cooking by preparing selected vegetable dishes.

PRODUCTS TO BE PREPARED TO ILLUSTRATE PRINCIPLES

Various methods of cooking carrots, red cabbage, onions, broccoli, and spinach
Harvard beets
Cauliflower with cheese sauce
Creamed green beans
Savory spinach
Baked potatoes: white, sweet
Buttered vegetables
Fried vegetables
Japanese-style vegetables with chicken and shrimp

PRINCIPLES

1. Pigments
   a. Classified by solubility:
      (1) Water insoluble (fat soluble).
          (a) Chlorophyll.
          (b) Carotenoid Group.
              (i) Carotene.
              (ii) Lycopene.
              (iii) Xanthophyll.
      (2) Water soluble (fat insoluble).
          (a) Anthocyanins.
          (b) Anthoxanthins (flavones).
   b. Color changes caused by:
      (1) Acids (plant acids, vinegar, cream of tartar).
      (2) Alkali (baking soda).
      (3) Minerals (iron, copper, zinc).
      (4) Enzymes.
      (5) Tannins.
      (6) Heat.

2. Tenderness
   a. Reactions of cellulose, hemicellulose, lignocellulose:
      (1) Heat plus moisture.
      (2) Affect of acid.
      (3) Affect of alkali.
   b. Change in pectic compounds (protopectin, pectin, pectic acid):
      (1) Maturation.
      (2) Heat plus moisture.
      (3) Affect of acid.
      (4) Affect of alkali.
      (5) Affect of calcium.
3. Texture
   a. Sloughing—varietal differences; affect of alkali (*see* Change in pectic compounds).
   b. Affect of acid—retention of structure and shape (*see* Change in pectic compounds).
   c. Affect of varietal differences, especially in potatoes, lima beans, and tomatoes.
4. Flavor
   a. Sulfur compounds:
      (1) Sinigrin—a glycoside (combination with a sugar) broken down to allylisothiocyanate and then to *hydrogen sulfide* by action of water and heat, resulting in an unpleasant flavor, which increases as cooking is extended.
      (2) Allyl sulfide—decomposes and dissipates, giving a milder flavor.
   b. Carbohydrates (sugar and starch):
      (1) Maturation—as vegetables mature, sugar is converted to starch, resulting in a bland flavor.
      (2) Storage temperature—especially important in potatoes, sweet corn, lima beans, and parsnips. As vegetables are held in cold storage, carbohydrate is retained as sugar, resulting in a sweet flavor. Sweetness is desirable in nearly all vegetables except white potatoes.
   c. Organic acids:
      (1) Oxalic acid.
      (2) Other plant acids.
   d. Other compounds:
      (1) Solanin
      (2) Organic compounds (aldehydes, alcohols, esters) occur in very small amounts; many are volatile and may be lost during cooking.
5. Method of cooking
   a. Boiling water:
      (1) Loss of water soluble nutrients.
      (2) Loss of some water soluble pigments.
   b. Steaming:
      (1) Increases length of cooking time.
      (2) Change in chlorophyll pigment.
      (3) Possibly better retention of shape.
      (4) Better retention of nutrients.
   c. Baking:
      (1) Possibly highest retention of nutrients.
      (2) Development of different type of flavor.

Beans, green	Trim off blossom and stem ends of each bean. (Discard brown spotted and/or wilted beans.) Wash thoroughly. Lift out of last wash water. Drain. Cut into 1–1 1/2-inch (2–4 cm) lengths.
Beets	Cut off stems and leaves 3 inches (7.5 cm) above the bulb. Brush bulb with vegetable brush holding the beets under running tap water. Do not remove the 3-inch (7.5 cm) portion of stem or root and do not peel the bulb before cooking. After beets have been cooked, drain off boiling water; add cold water to quickly cool cooked beets. When beets are cool enough to handle, with your fingers, slip off the skin of the beets (as you might peel a tangerine). Trim off long roots. Beets tend to "bleed" when cooking, so they are peeled after cooking.
Broccoli	Cut off approximately 1/4 inch (0.6 cm) slice from the stem end. Cut off coarse leaves. If outer portion of stem end is woody, strip off the woody outer portion up to the stem portion of the bud-blossom portion. Cut the stalk into two portions so the bud-blossom portion is 3–4 inches (7–10 cm) in length. (The heavier stem portion can be brought to a boil before the bud portions are added.) Wash thoroughly. Lift from last wash water.
Brussel sprouts	Trim off outer leaves if bruised or wilted. Look closely at stem end for insects; discard any infested sprouts. Wash trimmed sprouts thoroughly. To speed cooking, a 1/2-inch (1.3 cm) cut into the center of the sprout may be made at the stem end. Cut should almost bisect sprout, but not allow sprout to cook apart during the cooking period.
Cabbage	Trim off outer leaves if they are wilted. Wash cabbage thoroughly. For experimental work, cut into four equal wedges so each portion is held together by a portion of the heart of the cabbage. Cuts are made from stem end to top of cabbage.
Carrots and Parsnips	Remove a thin outer portion of the skin with a vegetable peeler. Trim off root end and stem end if necessary. Do not use any green portion from the stem end—this is bitter. Wash vegetable. For experimental work, cut carrots into disks approximately 1/4-inch (0.6 cm) thick. It is important that the thickness of the disks be standardized for the experimental work.
Cauliflower	Trim off outer leaf and/or vein portions. Wash thoroughly. Separate into floweret portions of about the same size.
Onions, dry	Remove outer layers of dry skin. Trim off root portion. For experimental work, all pieces should be of equal size. For small onions to be left whole, make a cut across the diameter of the onion at the stem end, about 1/2 inch (1.3 cm) toward the bottom of the onion. This allows for more rapid and even cooking. If onions are halved or quartered, retain a portion of the root section on each part to help hold the onion together.
Potatoes	*Baking*—hold potatoes under cold, running tap water and scrub with a vegetable brush. Dry skin with paper towels. *Boiling*—rinse unpeeled potatoes in cold water. Remove a thin layer of skin with a vegetable peeler. Any green portion should be cut away and discarded. Cut out discolored eyes. Wash peeled potatoes. Cut into approximately 1/2-inch (1.3 cm) cubes for rapid cooking in boiling water. Hold peeled potatoes in water to cover until ready to place in boiling water for cooking.
Rutabaga and Turnips	Use vegetable peeler to remove outer skin. Do not use any green portion. Cut approximately 1/2-inch (1.3 cm) cubes for cooking.
Spinach	Trim off heavy stem ends (and roots, if any). Place spinach leaves in a large panful of water. Rinse each leaf separately through the first wash water. Wash through at least two wash waters. Lift leaves out of water.
Zucchini	Thoroughly wash zucchini or other summer squash. Sand tends to cling to the zucchini skin. The zucchini is then ready to slice for sauteing or to parboil to stuff and bake.

PROCEDURES FOR BOILING SELECTED FRESH VEGETABLES

Vegetable	Size of Piece †	Amount of Water	Use of Cover	Boiling Time(Min)†
Asparagus	young, whole stalks	to barely cover	uncovered	10–15
Beans, green or yellow wax	2-inch (5 cm)	to barely cover	green—uncovered yellow wax—covered	15–20
Beets	Whole	1 inch (2.5 cm) more than vegetable	covered	45–60
Broccoli	4-inch (10 cm)	1 inch (2.5 cm) more than vegetable	uncovered	10–15
Brussels sprouts	whole	1 inch (2.5 cm) more than vegetable	uncovered	10–15
Cabbage, green or red*	2-inch (5 cm) wedge	2 inches (5 cm) more than vegetable	uncovered	8–15
Carrots	1/4-inch (0.6 cm) disks	to barely cover	covered	10–20
Cauliflower*	2-inch (5 cm) flowerets	2 inches (5 cm) more than vegetable	uncovered	8–15
Corn on the cob	whole ear	1 inch (2.5 cm) more than vegetable	covered	3–5
Onions*	1-inch (2.5 cm) dia.	1 inch (2.5 cm) more than vegetable	uncovered	10–15
Parsnips	3–4 inch (7–10 cm) lengths; halve or quarter each length depending on diameter	to barely cover	covered	10–20
Peas	whole	to barely cover	uncovered	10–15
Potatoes, white*	1-inch (2.5 cm) cubes	to barely cover	covered	10–15
Rutabaga	3/4-inch (2 cm) cubes	1 inch (2.5 cm) more than vegetable	uncovered	10–20
Spinach	leaves	1/2 inch (1.3 cm) deep in saucepan	covered for 3 min.; then remove cover	5–8
Squash, summer varieties**	1/4-inch (0.6 cm) disks	1/2 inch (1.3 cm) deep in saucepan	**covered or **uncovered	5–8
Turnips*	3/4-inch (2 cm) cubes	1 inch (2.5 cm) more than vegetable	uncovered	10–20

Note: Use 1/4 teaspoon (1 ml) salt per cup (250 ml) water. Add cleaned vegetable to boiling water. Count time when water returns to boil.

*May add 1/8–1/4 teaspoon (0.5–1 ml) cream of tartar for better color.

†Total cooking time is always related to size of piece.

**Yellow and white—covered; green—uncovered.

Vegetables—Effect of Cooking Treatment

Red cabbage—1/2 medium head
Carrots—8 medium
Broccoli—1 bunch
Onions—8 medium
Spinach, fresh—2 10-ounce packages (500 g)
Cream of tartar
Soda
Vinegar

1. Put 1 quart (1 L) cold water in a 2-quart (2 L) saucepan and bring to a boil; start 1 pan for each treatment.
2. Clean vegetables.
3. Divide carrots, red cabbage, onions, and spinach into four equal portions. Divide the broccoli into five equal portions.
4. For each treatment listed below, cook one portion of vegetable; add vegetables to boiling water.
5. It may be necessary to add more hot water if substantial amounts of water are lost by evaporation. *Do not* let the vegetable boil dry.
6. At the end of the cooking period, drain the vegetable by placing it in a strainer. Collect part of the cooking liquid in a glass custard cup. Put the cooked vegetable on a white plate for evaluation. (It is important that all samples of one vegetable be on the same type of plate for comparative evaluation.)
*7. Evaluation and discussions should include both the cooked vegetable and the cooking liquid.
8. Record observations in the tables on the following pages.

*To illustrate reversibility of anthocyanin pigment in presence of acid, put two or three leaves of red cabbage cooked by treatments 1, 2, or 3 on a small white plate. Evenly spread 1 tablespoon (15 ml) of vinegar over leaves. Allow to stand 5–10 minutes. Note the increase in redness.

Cooking Treatments**

1. Boil for 15 minutes. Count time after water returns to a boil.
2. Boil for 30 minutes. Count time after water returns to a boil.
3. Add 1/2 teaspoon (2 ml) baking soda after adding the water. Boil for 15 minutes after water returns to a boil.
4. Add 1 teaspoon (5 ml) cream of tartar after adding the water. Boil for 15 minutes after water returns to a boil.
5. For the fifth sample of broccoli, place a lid on the saucepan after the water has been added: boil for 30 minutes after water returns to a boil.

**In this particular lesson, cooking treatments have been standardized so that direct comparisons on the effect of treatment can be made. Length of cooking time is a more objective method to achieve standardization than the degree of tenderness ("cook until crisp tender"). Cover saucepan for cooking carrots; use uncovered saucepan for all other samples.

Steaming Vegetables*—General Directions

1. Place 1-2 inches (2-5 cm) of water in lower section of steamer. Enough water must be used to produce steam for entire cooking time.
2. Place cleaned vegetable in steamer basket; position over water. Tightly cover pan.
3. Bring water quickly to boiling over high heat. When water is boiling, reduce heat to keep water boiling slowly.
4. Cooking time for steaming vegetables is approximately 50% longer than if the vegetable is boiled in water.

Caution: When opening steamer, tilt the lid so it prevents steam from rising in your face.

Baked Potatoes* (See page 255 for Microwave Method.)

1. Preheat oven to 400°F (200°C). If time is an important factor, a higher oven temperature, up to 450°F (230°C), may be used. However, potatoes must be carefully checked so they do not get too hot. The oven can be preheated to 450°F (230°C) and heat can be lowered to 400°F (200°C) after 10 minutes cooking.
2. Place washed, dried potatoes on a shallow baking pan. Do not crowd potatoes on the baking sheet.
3. Bake until the potatoes can be pierced readily with a fork. Medium-sized potatoes in a 400°F (200°C) oven may require 1-1 1/2 hours to bake.
    Note:
    a. If potato skins are to be eaten, a small amount of fat can be rubbed over the surface of the potato skin to give a more tender skin on the baked potato.
    b. If potatoes are freshly harvested, they may have a high water content. These potatoes tend to explode in the oven. If these potatoes are pricked with a fork about halfway through the baking period, they will have less tendency to explode in the oven.
4. As soon as potatoes are removed from the oven, the potatoes should be slit open to allow steam to escape and prevent the potatoes from becoming soggy.
5. Record total working time:_____ minutes.

*Suggest using a high-solids variety (Russet), a low-solids variety (Red Pontiac), and a sweet potato or yam for baking.

CHARACTERISTICS OF HIGH QUALITY BAKED WHITE POTATOES

Appearance: White, opaque or slightly translucent depending on variety.
Texture: Cell structure is friable; mealy; light.
Moistness: Dry.
Flavor: Bland, yet *slightly* sweet.

CHARACTERISTICS OF HIGH QUALITY BAKED SWEET POTATOES

Appearance: Yellow to orange; slightly translucent.
Texture: Solid or compact.
Moistness: Moist to wet depending on variety.
Flavor: Sweet; may be slightly caramelized.

OBSERVATIONS ON VEGETABLES

Vegetable	Treatment Number	Color		Texture	Flavor
		Juice	Vegetable		
Red cabbage Pigment: Flavor constituent:	(1) 15 minutes				
	(2) 30 minutes				
	(3) soda				
	(4) acid				
Onions Pigment: Flavor constituent:	(1) 15 minutes				
	(2) 30 minutes				
	(3) soda				
	(4) acid				
Carrots Pigment: Flavor constituent:	(1) 15 minutes				
	(2) 30 minutes				
	(3) soda				
	(4) acid				

Vegetable	Treatment Number	Color		Texture	Flavor
		Juice	Vegetable		
Broccoli Pigment: Flavor constituent:	(1) 15 minutes uncovered				
	(2) 30 minutes uncovered				
	(3) soda uncovered				
	(4) acid uncovered				
	(5) 30 minutes covered				
Spinach Pigment: Flavor constituent:	(1) 15 minutes				
	(2) 30 minutes				
	(3) soda				
	(4) acid				

BAKED POTATOES

Variety	Appearance	Moistness and Texture	Flavor

Buttered Vegetables

1. Cook vegetable according to directions, page 170.
2. Allow 1/2–1 teaspoon (2–5 ml) butter or margarine for each serving.
3. Place the hot, cooked, and drained vegetable in its serving dish. Add the butter or margarine.
4. Stir lightly so the fat melts evenly throughout the vegetable.*
5. *Do not* have the vegetable swimming in fat.
6. Record total working time:_____minutes.

*For four or more servings, the butter or margarine can be melted before it is added to the hot, cooked vegetable.

Creamed Vegetables

Vegetable, cooked 2 cups (500 ml)	1/2 pound	225 g
Milk	1 cup	250 ml
Butter or margarine	2 tablespoons	30 ml
Flour	2 tablespoons	30 ml
Salt	1/4 teaspoon	1 ml

1. Cook vegetable according to directions, page 170.
2. Melt fat in a saucepan; add flour and salt; stir thoroughly to blend.
3. Remove from heat; add milk gradually; stir well after each addition to get a smooth paste.
4. Bring to a boil over direct heat; boil for 1 minute with constant stirring.
5. Add cooked, drained vegetable. Add more salt if necessary.
6. Heat to serving. Sauce should have consistency of whipping cream before whipping. Add more milk if necessary to obtain the correct consistency.
7. Record total working time:_____minutes.

Cauliflower or Broccoli with Cheese Sauce (See page 256 for Microwave Method.)

Cauliflower or broccoli, cooked	1/2 pound	225 g
Milk	1 cup	250 ml
Butter or margarine	2 tablespoons	30 ml
Flour	2 tablespoons	30 ml
Salt	1/4 teaspoon	1 ml
Cheddar cheese, grated	1/2 cup	125 ml

1. Cook vegetable according to directions, page 170. Drain thoroughly.
2. Melt fat in saucepan; add flour and salt; blend thoroughly.
3. Remove from heat; add milk in portions; stir thoroughly after each addition to form a smooth paste.
4. Bring to a boil over direct heat; boil for 1 minute with constant stirring.
5. Remove from heat. Add grated cheese. Stir until blended.
6. Place the hot, cooked cauliflower or broccoli in a warm serving dish. Pour hot cheese sauce over the vegetable. Use only sufficient sauce to cover vegetable. *Do not* drown vegetable in sauce.
7. Record total working time:_____minutes.

Harvard Beets

Beets, cooked or canned	2 cups	500 ml
Liquid from beets (or water)	1/2 cup	125 ml
Cornstarch	1 tablespoon + 1 teaspoon	20 ml
Sugar	2 tablespoons	30 ml
Salt	1/2 teaspoon	2 ml
Vinegar	1/4 cup	50 ml
Butter or margarine	1 tablespoon	15 ml

1. Blend together the liquid, cornstarch, sugar, and salt in a saucepan.
2. Bring to a boil over direct heat with constant stirring. The mixture should boil until it is clear.
3. Remove from heat; add margarine and vinegar; stir to blend; add cooked beets.
4. Heat over low heat until the beets are heated through.
5. Record total working time:_____ minutes.

Sweet-Sour Red Cabbage

Red cabbage, finely shredded (not grated)	1 pound	450 g
Apple, tart, medium size, chopped fine	1	1
Brown sugar	3 tablespoons	45 ml
Vinegar	3 tablespoons	45 ml
Cornstarch	2 teaspoons	10 ml
Caraway seeds (optional)	1/2 teaspoon	2 ml
Cooking liquid or water	1/2 cup	125 ml

1. Place shredded cabbage and chopped apple together in a saucepan; add boiling water for approximately 1/2-inch (1.3 cm) water in pan. Cook rapidly, uncovered, until cabbage is crisp tender. Add more boiling water as necessary. Stir through cabbage with a fork for even cooking. Drain.
2. Combine brown sugar and cornstarch; add cold water or cooled cooking liquid. Bring mixture to a boil and boil 1 minute. Add vinegar; blend. Add to cooked cabbage. Heat to serving temperature. If caraway seeds are used, add for this last heating period.
3. Record total working time:_____ minutes.

Savory Spinach (See page 255 for Microwave Method.)

Spinach, fresh, cooked, drained raw weight	1 1/2 pounds	675 g
Bacon	4 slices	4 slices
Onion, small, thinly sliced	1	1
Sweet pickle relish	2 tablespoons	30 ml

1. Cook vegetable according to directions, page 170.
2. Cut bacon into small pieces with a scissors. Place in an electric frying pan. Add the onion slices. Cook over low heat until the bacon is crisp and the onion is tender.
3. Stir in the sweet pickle and the cooked, drained spinach. Reheat if necessary.
4. Record total working time:_____minutes.

Fried Parsnips

Parsnips	1 pound	450 g
Butter or margarine	2 tablespoons	30 ml

1. Clean and cook parsnips in salted water (see page 169). Cook parsnips in same fry pan in which the vegetable will be browned. Use only enough water to cook parsnips so most of all the water evaporates by the time the parsnips are tender.
2. When parsnips are tender, remove any excess water left in fry pan. Add the butter or margarine to the fry pan. Work melted fat under each piece of vegetable. Fry over low heat until parsnips are golden brown. Parsnips brown more evenly if only a single layer is fried at one time.
3. If glazed parsnips are desired, add up to 2 tablespoons (30 ml) sugar to the fry pan as parsnips are browning. Avoid overcaramelization of the sugar.
4. Record total working time:_____minutes.

Pan-Fried Eggplant

Eggplant, medium	1	1
Salt	1 1/2 teaspoons	7 ml
Egg	1	1
Water	2 tablespoons	30 ml
Fine crumbs	1 cup	250 ml
Butter or margarine	1/4 cup	50 ml

1. Wash and dry eggplant. Cut into 1/4-inch (0.6 cm) slices; peel each slice and place on a plate; sprinkle each slice with some of the salt; allow to stand for 15 minutes. Rinse salt from eggplant; dry each slice with paper toweling.
2. Break egg onto a flat plate; add water; blend egg and water using a fork.
3. Dip each slice of eggplant in egg mixture so both sides are immersed.
4. Have fine crumbs on either waxed paper or a flat plate.
5. Transfer egg-coated eggplant slices to fine crumbs. Coat each side with crumbs.
6. Melt about half the butter or margarine in a heavy fry pan; have surface of pan covered with a thin layer of fat. Fat should be hot but *not* smoking as slices of eggplant are added. Carefully brown slices on each side; add more butter or margarine as necessary. Slices may be tender after they have been browned; reduce heat for further cooking as necessary.
7. Avoid using too much fat. Eggplant has the ability to absorb fat as a sponge absorbs water.
8. Record total working time:_____minutes.

Sauteed Onions (See page 140 for recipe and directions.)

*Japanese Style Vegetables with Chicken and Shrimp

**Water	1 cup	250 ml
Soy sauce	4 tablespoons	60 ml
Sugar	3 tablespoons	45 ml
Salt (optional)	1/2 teaspoon	2 ml
Raw shrimp, peeled & deveined	6	6
Snow peas, fresh	1 cup	250 ml
Sherry, dry (optional)	1/4 cup	50 ml
Chicken	1 1/2 pounds	680 g
Cauliflower, precooked	1 cup	250 ml
Mushrooms, fresh	10	10

1. Skin and bone the chicken, cut into bite-size pieces. Peel and devein the shrimp.
2. Clean cauliflower, break into flowerets; boil for 4–5 minutes. Wash and stem the snow peas. Clean, trim, rinse under running water and slice the mushrooms.
3. Mix in a bowl; water, 3 tablespoons (45 ml) soy sauce, sugar and salt.
4. Set all ingredients by the WOK in the order listed.
5. Set WOK on high (400°F); heat for 60 seconds and add the water mixture; bring to a boil.
†6. Add shrimp, boil until pink and opaque (about 3 minutes).
7. Remove with a slotted spoon to a heated serving plate; keep warm in an oven set at 200°F.
8. Add snow peas, sherry, and chicken, bring to boil; stir and cook for 5 minutes. Remove to the heated serving dish; sprinkle with the remaining soy sauce. Return to the oven.
9. If water is low, add a little. Add cauliflower and mushrooms and cook 3–4 minutes; remove to heated serving dish.
10. Arrange all the cooked products separately on the platter. Pour cooking liquid into a small pitcher and serve immediately.
11. Record total working time:_____ minutes.

*1. This recipe may be stir-fried in an electric fry pan (Teflon® coated) if a WOK is not available.
**2. When water, bouillon, or broth are used in place of oil, "stir-frying" in reality becomes a moist heat method for cooking the meat, poultry, or fish included in the recipe.
3. Rice may be served with this recipe; see page 100.
†4. Shrimp may be cut into halves or thirds.

Fried Zucchini

Zucchini or Summer Squash	1/2 pound	225 g
Butter or margarine	2 tablespoons	30 ml
Salt	1/4 teaspoon	1 ml

1. Thoroughly wash zucchini or squash to remove all dirt and sand. Dry with paper toweling.
2. Slice squash into 1/4-inch (0.6 cm) disks. Do not pare.
3. Melt fat in a heavy frying pan, over medium-low heat.
4. Add squash to melted fat; sprinkle salt over squash. Slices of squash may be browned on one or both sides. Cook until tender, 20–25 minutes.*
5. Record total working time:_____minutes.

*Fry pan may be covered during cooking. Cook over medium-low heat 15–20 minutes or until squash is tender. The vegetables are cooked by steam in this technique.

CHARACTERISTICS OF HIGH QUALITY COOKED VEGETABLES

Appearance: Pieces intact; cut edge remains distinct; color is typical of predominant pigment present.
Texture: Cell structure softens without disintegrating.
Tenderness: Tender, yet slightly firm to bite. Vegetables cooked by "stir-frying" are usually more crisp than vegetables that are sauteed or cooked by other methods.
Flavor: Predominant flavor constituent of the raw vegetable may or may not predominate in the cooked vegetable; many vegetables may have a slightly sweet note.

CHARACTERISTICS OF HIGH QUALITY VEGETABLE SAUCES

Cream sauces (See page 92.):

Cheese sauce:

Appearance: Color (cheddar cheese in sauce) is a pale apricot (yellow-orange); opaque. Fat remains evenly dispersed throughout the sauce. Cheese is evenly dispersed throughout the sauce.
Consistency: Slightly thicker than heavy whipping cream; flows slowly but is fluid; starch granules are evenly distributed and gelatinized.
Flavor: Distinct cheese flavor which blends with flavor of vegetable.

Vinegar sauce on Harvard beets:

Appearance: Clear, translucent, bright, dark red color.
Consistency: Slightly thinner than whipping cream; starch granules are evenly distributed and gelatinized.
Flavor: Tart but with a sweet note; beet flavor will be more distinct when the liquid from the canned beets is used in the sauce.

Note: See page 199 for Review Questions.

Dried Legumes

OBJECTIVES

1. To demonstrate the three stages of preparation essential to transform dried legumes into meal service products:
   a. Rehydration.
   b. Cooking in water until tender.
   c. Cooking with seasonings to increase palatability.
2. To illustrate use of legumes as meat substitutes; therefore, no meat will be used in the recipes that follow.
3. To discuss high nutrient value of dried legumes.
4. To acquaint students with a variety of legumes.

PRODUCTS TO BE PREPARED TO ILLUSTRATE PRINCIPLES

Blackeye beans southern style
Lentils and rice with tomatoes
Curried kidney beans
Western bean stew
Barbecued lima beans

PRINCIPLES

1. Dried legumes must be hydrated before cooking. Some legumes are commerically processed to reduce hydration time.
*2. Soda may be added to speed hydration. Before legumes are cooked, soda must be rinsed off to prevent vitamin destruction and cell disintegration by alkali.
3. Legumes must be cooked tender in plain water before ingredients containing acids or calcium are added because:
   a. Insoluble calcium pectate can be formed by addition of molasses, brown sugar, or canned tomatoes.
   b. Insoluble pectic substances can be formed by addition of tomatoes, tomato sauce, catsup, or vinegar.
4. Insoluble pectic compounds can be formed if water in which beans have been cooked contains calcium or magnesium ions.

*Use 1/4 teaspoon (1 ml) soda per quart of water for soaking. Rinse legumes carefully to *remove* soda before cooking.

Blackeye Beans Southern Style

Blackeye beans, dry	1 cup	250 ml
or cooked	3 cups	750 ml
Water to soak dry beans	3 cups	750 ml
*Bacon fat or lard or shortening	1 tablespoon	15 ml
Flour	1 teaspoon	5 ml
Salt	3/4 teaspoon	3 ml
Pepper, black	1/4 teaspoon	1 ml
Cayenne pepper	few grains	few grains
Onion, medium, minced	1	1

1. Sort and wash beans. Cover beans with water; bring to a boil; boil 2 minutes. Turn off heat; cover saucepan and allow beans to stand for 1 hour. (*Alternate method:* Soak washed beans overnight before cooking).
2. Melt bacon fat in a heavy skillet, stir in flour, seasonings and onions. Cook until onions are lightly browned.
3. Pour onion mixture into beans; cover; simmer until beans are tender, approximately 1 hour.
4. Record total working time:_____minutes. Yield: 3-4 servings.

*Use bacon fat or lard for authentic Southern style; use vegetable shortening for vegetarian product.

Lentils and Rice with Tomatoes

Lentils, dry	1 cup	250 ml
or cooked	3 cups	750 ml
Water to soak dry lentils	3 cups	750 ml
Bay leaf	1	1
Parsley	3 sprigs	3 sprigs
Onion, medium, finely chopped	1	1
Margarine or oil	3 tablespoons	45 ml
Rice	1/3 cup	75 ml
Nutmeg, ground	1/4 teaspoon	1 ml
Salt	1 teaspoon	5 ml
Pepper, black	few grains	few grains
Tomatoes, canned	1 cup	250 ml

1. Sort and wash lentils. Soak overnight.
2. Do not rinse; add bay leaf, parsley, and salt; cook until lentils are tender, approximately 1 hour.
3. Add the rice to 1 cup (250 ml) boiling salted water (use 1/4 teaspoon or 1 ml salt for each cup water). Cook over low heat until rice is tender. One teaspoon (5 ml) butter or margarine can be added while the rice is cooking.
4. Melt fat in a heavy frying pan or a flame-proof casserole. Add onion; saute until onion is lightly browned. Do *not* burn.
5. Add all other ingredients. Either simmer all ingredients together for 15 minutes or bake for 30 minutes in a 350°F (175°C) oven.
6. Remove bay leaf and cooked parsley before serving.
7. Record total working time:_____ minutes. Yield: 3-4 servings.

Curried Kidney Beans

Kidney beans, dry	1 cup	250	ml
or cooked	3 cups	750	ml
Water to soak dry beans	3 cups	750	ml
Salt	1 teaspoon	5	ml
Onion, medium, sliced	1	1	
Pepper	1/8 teaspoon	0.5	ml
Curry powder	1/2–1 teaspoon	2–5	ml
Shortening or oil	2 tablespoons	30 ml	

1. Sort and wash kidney beans. Soak overnight in water to cover. (*Alternate method:* Cover beans with water; bring to a boil; boil 2 minutes. Turn off heat; cover pan; let beans stand for 1 hour.)
2. Add salt to soaked beans. Cook beans until tender, about 1 hour. Drain. Reserve liquid.
3. Melt fat in heavy frying pan. Add onion; saute until onion is slightly yellow, about 5 minutes.
4. Add cooked beans, pepper, curry powder and 1/2 cup (125 ml) bean liquid. Simmer together 15–30 minutes for blending of flavors. Add bean liquid as necessary. Beans should be moist but not soupy when served.
5. Record total working time: _____ minutes. Yield: 3–4 servings.

Western Bean Stew

Pinto or cranberry beans, dry	1 cup	250 ml
or cooked	3 cups	750 ml
Water to soak dry beans	3 cups	750 ml
Salt	1/2 teaspoon	2 ml
Tabasco sauce	2–3 drops	2–3 drops
Shortening	2 tablespoons	30 ml
Onion, medium, chopped	1	1
Garlic, small clove, minced	1	1
Tomatoes, canned	1 cup	250 ml
Parsley, minced	2 tablespoons	30 ml
Marjoram, ground	1/4 teaspoon	1 ml
Chili powder	1 teaspoon	5 ml

1. Sort and wash beans. Soak overnight in enough water to cover beans.
2. Add salt and tabasco sauce to beans; bring to boil; reduce heat; simmer until beans are tender, approximately 1 hour. Drain beans and reserve liquid.
3. While beans are cooking, melt fat in a heavy frying pan; add onions and garlic; cook until onion is light yellow. Add tomatoes, parsley, 1/2 cup (125 ml) of the reserved bean liquid, and the spices; simmer together 30 minutes.
4. Add beans to onion mixture; simmer together for an additional 15 minutes.
5. Record total working time: _____ minutes. Yield: 3–4 servings.

Barbecued Lima Beans

Lima beans, dry	1 cup	250 ml
or cooked	3 cups	750 ml
Water to soak dry beans	3 cups	750 ml
Onion, medium, minced	1	1
Garlic, small clove, minced	1	1
Oil or margarine	2 tablespoons	30 ml
Brown sugar	3 tablespoons	45 ml
Vinegar, cider	2 tablespoons	30 ml
Mustard, prepared	1 teaspoon	5 ml
Tomato sauce—8 ounce (227 g) can	1	1
Tomatoes, canned or juice	1/2 cup	125 ml

1. Sort and wash beans. Soak overnight in enough water to cover beans.
2. Cook beans in salted water (1/4 teaspoon salt or 1 ml salt per cup of water) until beans are tender. Start with approximately 1 inch of water above beans. Drain cooked beans.
3. Melt fat or heat oil in heavy frying pan or flame-proof casserole; add onion and garlic; cook slowly until onion is yellow and transparent but not browned.
4. Add all other ingredients to onion mixture; simmer over low heat for 30 minutes or bake in a 350°F (175°C) oven approximately 1 hour for a blending of flavors.
5. Record total working time: _____ minutes. Yield: 4–6 servings.

CHARACTERISTICS OF HIGH QUALITY DRIED LEGUME PRODUCTS

Appearance: Beans or lentils retain shape. Liquid well absorbed by legumes (unless a stew or soup product).
Texture: Dried legumes (except soybeans) are mealy.
Tenderness: Little resistance to bite.
*****Flavor:** Distinctive for variety or type of legume; seasonings well blended.

*Flavor would be improved with longer cooking time than is available in the laboratory period.

REVIEW QUESTIONS

1. What are dried legumes?
2. Discuss briefly the nutritional value of dried legumes.
3. Why are dried legumes soaked in water to which soda has been added?
4. What would happen when the legumes are cooked if the soda was not rinsed off?
5. Why are legumes cooked tender before the addition of flavoring substances (i.e., molasses, tomato)?

Fruits

OBJECTIVES

1. To study the relationship between varietal characteristics of apples and the quality characteristics of selected cooked apple products.
2. To study the factors which affect the cooking of dehydrated fruits.
3. To illustrate the effect of sugar on cell structure.
4. To observe and study conditions which affect enzymatic browning in certain lightcolored, fresh, pared, and/or sliced fruit.
5. To study factors affecting formation of pectin gels.

PRODUCTS TO BE PREPARED TO ILLUSTRATE PRINCIPLES

*Raw apples—varietal differences
Raw apples—enzymatic browning
Apple sauce
Coddled apples
Baked apples
Prunes
Cranberry sauce
Cranberry jelly

PRINCIPLES

1. In cooking fruits, softening of cell structure results from:
   a. Breakdown of protopectin (cell cementing substance).
   b. Softening of hemicellulose.
2. Agitation during cooking may cause rupturing of cell structure.
3. By osmosis:
   a. Water may pass into cell structure to cause a rupturing of the cell. (No sugar present during the cooking period.)
   b. Sugar may pass into cell structure to cause a firming of the cell. (When fruit is cooked in a dilute sugar syrup.)
   c. Sugar in dry form or in concentrated solution may cause dehydration of cell structure, which results in a hard, tough piece of cooked fruit.
4. Sugar and pectin (in the fruit juice) in proper amounts will product a jelly structure.

*Select apple varieties to include: (1) an all-purpose, (2) a cooking, and (3) an eating (raw) variety.

5. Light-colored fresh fruits (apples, apricots, avocados, peaches, pears) darken when exposed to air as a result of the presence of oxidative enzymes. Browning is delayed by coating the cut surface.
   a. Hold slices of fruit under cold water until ready to use.
   b. Dip fruit slices in citrus juice.
   c. Combine with commercial ascorbic acid preparations.
   d. Immerse in sugar syrup.
6. Dehydrated fruits (prunes, apricots, apples, pears, raisins) must have water absorbed by plant tissue before the fruit will become soft as a result of cooking. Very dry fruit will require a longer time to absorb water. "Moisturized" fruits may require very short or no special hydration period before they will cook tender in water or steam.
7. Dehydrated and dehydrofrozen fruits will absorb water more rapidly if hot water is added to the fruit for the hydration period.

FRUITS—VARIABLES

Dried Fruits
1. Fruit soaked overnight to rehydrate.
2. Fruit soaked 20 minutes in hot water to rehydrate.

Fresh Fruits
*1. Apples
    a. Sauce prepared from varieties of apples:
        (1) Cooking variety—rapid rate of disintegration of cell structure.
        (2) Cooking variety—slow rate of disintegration of cell structure.
        (3) All-purpose variety—moderate rate of disintegration of cell structure.
        (4) Eating raw variety—not suited for cooking.
    b. Coddled apples—same varieties as listed above.
    c. Baked apples—same varieties as listed above.
    d. Evaluate all varieties in raw form.
    e. Use each variety to illustrate effectiveness of ascorbic acid solution to delay enzymatic browning. Hold cut slices at least 30 minutes before evaluating.
        (1) Raw apple slices not treated.
        (2) Raw apple slices dipped in ascorbic acid solution.
2. Cranberries
    a. Sauce prepared from whole berries:
        (1) Fruit cooked in boiling water, sugar added after cooking.
        (2) Fruit cooked in sugar syrup.
    b. Jelly prepared by cooking fruit in water; straining fruit to remove seeds and skins; adding sugar and cooking to jelly stage.

*Raw apples continue to respire in any type of storage. Apples used shortly after harvest will be of higher quality than apples held in storage. The longer the storage period, the greater the decrease in quality. Respiration is slowest under controlled atmosphere storage.

Browning Reactions in Fresh Fruits

*Apples, for each variety being cooked—2 to 4
Ascorbic acid, commercial mix—1 teaspoon (5 ml)

1. Follow package directions for preparation of the ascorbic acid solution. Prepare 1 or 2 cups (250 or 500 ml) of solution.
2. Wash and dry apples. Cut into quarters. Core.
3. Cut each quarter into 3-5 slices. For half the samples of each variety, dip the slices of apple into the ascorbic acid solution *immediately* after slicing. Remove slices from solution after each side of slice has been wetted. Arrange on a plate. *Do not* cover. Let stand at least 30 minutes (1 hour preferred) before comparing with products from the second treatment.
4. Arrange the remaining apple slices on a plate as they are cut. *Do not* cover. Allow to remain exposed to air for at least 30 minutes (1 hour preferred).
5. Compare the appearance (surface browning) by the two treatments. Also note whether variety is a factor.

*Avocados, apricots, pears, peaches, or bananas may be substituted for apples.

Applesauce (See page 254 for Microwave Method.)

Apples, medium size	3	3
Water, boiling	3/4 cup	175 ml
Sugar	3 tablespoons	45 ml
No spice for class work		

1. Wash, pare, and cut each apple into 12 to 16 sections.* Core each slice. Cut apples in half from stem end to blossom end. Cut each half into two pieces (quarter of whole apple). Cut each quarter into 3 or 4 equal slices.
2. Add apple slices to boiling water; cover saucepan; cook at simmering, 185°–200°F (85°–95°C), temperature until slices are tender and soft—approximately 15 to 20 minutes.
3. Stir cooked apple slices with a fork until slices are broken up. Add sugar and stir until sugar is dissolved.
4. No spice is used for class work so the natural flavor of apples of several varieties can be tested and compared.
5. Record total working time: _____ minutes.

*Some applesauce can be made with apples unpeeled. Wash apples; cut into uniform sized slices without paring the apples. Apple skins may or may not be removed before sugar is added.

CHARACTERISTICS OF HIGH QUALITY APPLESAUCE

Appearance: Bright yellow color, the shade of yellow depending on the variety of apple used; pieces of apple pulp should be of uniform size, usually quite small with all the water absorbed by the pulp.
Consistency and Texture: Small even-size pieces of pulp, not easily identifiable; a spoonful mounds up when put on a plate.
Tenderness: Soft, no resistance to bite.
Flavor: Apple flavor identifiable and not masked by sweetness or spice flavor when spices are used.

Coddled Apples

Apples, medium size	2	2
Sugar	2/3 cup	150 ml
Water	1 1/2 cups	375 ml

1. Add sugar to water in a wide-bottomed saucepan. Stir until sugar is dissolved. Bring to a boil.
2. Wash, pare, core, and cut into 1/4-inch (0.6 cm) rings.
3. Add apples to hot sirup and cover saucepan. Reduce heat so apples cook slowly for about 20 minutes or until apple slices are translucent and clear.
4. Record total working time: _____ minutes.

CHARACTERISTICS OF HIGH QUALITY CODDLED APPLES

Appearance: Slices intact; translucent, bright yellow color, the shade of yellow dependent on the variety of apple used.
Texture: Just firm enough to remain intact.
Tenderness: Slightly firm, little resistance to bite.
Flavor: Apple flavor identifiable and not masked by sweetness.

Baked Apples

Apples, medium size	2	2
Sugar	1/4 cup	50 ml
Water	2 teaspoons	10 ml

No spice added for class work

1. Preheat oven to 450°F (230°C).
2. Wash and core apples (use special coring device).
3. Further prepare apples for baking.
   a. On one apple at the blossom end, pare off about 1 1/2 inch (3.8 cm) of skin.
   b. On the second apple, barely cut through the skin around the circumference of the apple, midway between stem and blossom ends.
4. Place the apples in a baking dish.*
5. Fill center cavity of each apple with 2 tablespoons (30 ml) of sugar.
6. Slightly moisten the sugar in each apple with 1 teaspoon (5 ml) of water.
7. Add water to baking dish so bottom of dish is covered with 1/4 inch (0.6 cm) of water.
8. Cover baking dish with aluminum foil for at least the first half of the baking period.
9. Bake at 450°F (230°C) for 10 minutes; reduce oven setting to 350°F (175°C); bake 40–50 minutes or until apples are tender. See footnote item 3.*
10. Record total working time: _____ minutes.

*(1) For class discussion, all varieties of apples should be baked in one large baking dish.
(2) Identify varieties of apples by marking outside of baking pan with marking pencil.
(3) All varieties of apples do not bake to similar degrees of tenderness within a controlled time limit. This is one way to illustrate varietal differences in apples. Remove the pan of apples from the oven when the all-purpose variety is fork tender.

CHARACTERISTICS OF HIGH QUALITY BAKED APPLES

Appearance: Apple must remain intact; skin color red to brownish-red depending on variety of apple used.
Tenderness: *Skin:* little resistance to bite. *Pulp:* smooth, soft, no resistance to bite.
Flavor: Apple flavor identifiable and not overpowered by sweetness or spice flavor when spices are used.

*Cranberries—For Each Variable

Cranberries, all edible portion	1 cup	250 ml
Water	1/2 cup	125 ml
Sugar	1/2 cup	125 ml

*Cranberries purchased in season, frozen, and used at a later date will give satisfactory results. Certain varieties of grapes (Concord), crab apples, currants, gooseberries, or loganberries may be substituted for cranberries.

*Fruit Sauce (Cooked in Water)
1. Sort and wash cranberries.
2. Add water and bring to a boil. Boil for 5 minutes or until the skins have popped open.
3. Add sugar and stir until the sugar is dissolved. Simmer, 185°-200°F (85°-95°C), for 5 minutes.
4. Pour into serving dish. Allow to cool before evaluating.
5. Record total working time:_____ minutes.

*Fruit Sauce (Cooked in Syrup)
1. Sort and wash cranberries.
2. Bring water and sugar to a boil. Stir until the sugar is dissolved.
3. Add cranberries to the boiling syrup. Skins will tend to pop open. Cook at 200°-212°F (95°-100°C) for 5 minutes. *Do not* over stir while the fruit is cooking.
4. Pour into serving dish. Allow to cool before comparing with other products.
5. Record total working time: _____ minutes.

*Compare the tenderness of the cranberry skins for the fruit cooked by each of these methods.

Jelly (Fruit Strained)
1. Sort and wash cranberries.
2. Add water. Bring to a boil: boil for 5 minutes or until the skins have popped open.
3. Rub the cooked berries through a strainer or put through a food mill, collecting the juice and as much of the pulp as possible in a clean saucepan placed underneath.
4. Add sugar to sieved pulp. Stir until sugar is dissolved.
5. Heat quickly to boiling temperature and boil for about 5 minutes. Mixture may need to be stirred constantly to prevent fruit pulp from sticking to bottom of saucepan and to keep mixture from spattering as it boils.
6. At the end of the cooking period, the mixture should give a jelly "sheeting" test: several drops of juice tend to flow together from the side of the spoon. (Cook until this test is reached.)
7. Pour into a serving dish. *Do not* stir this mixture as it cools.
8. Record total working time: _____ minutes.

CHARACTERISTICS OF HIGH QUALITY CRANBERRY SAUCE

Appearance: Deep red; translucence is masked by seeds and pulp.
Texture: *Cooked in water:* fluid, no gel structure. *Cooked in syrup:* thicker, may have a tendency to gel.
Tenderness: Skins should be tender with little resistance to bite.
Flavor: Typical of fruit, tart.

CHARACTERISTICS OF HIGH QUALITY CRANBERRY JELLY

† **Appearance:** Deep red translucent; seeds may or may not be present.
Consistency and Texture: Firm gel, should hold a cut edge; syneresis at a minimum.
Tenderness: Firm yet soft.
Flavor: Typical of fruit, tart.

† Will depend on size opening of food mill or strainer used after the fruit is cooked.

Prunes—Not Soaked

Prunes, per person	1	1
Water to cover fruit—approximately	1 1/2 cups	375 ml
Sugar—adjust as necessary	1/4 cup	50 ml
Lemon, optional, thin slices	2	2

1. Wash fruit in warm tap water. Lift fruit pieces out of wash water.
2. Add cold water to dried fruit. Quickly heat until water begins to boil. Turn off heat. Cover saucepan with a tight-fitting cover. Allow saucepan to remain on warm burner with the heat off. Soak fruit for 25 minutes.
3. Simmer, 185°–200°F (85°–90°C), fruit for 40 minutes. Keep saucepan covered. Add more hot water as needed. *Do not* allow to cook dry.
4. Remove cover from saucepan. Add sugar, if used.
5. Simmer in an uncovered saucepan for 3 minutes after sugar has been added. (A thin slice of lemon may be added to prunes at the same time as the sugar is added.)
6. If the liquid on the fruit is watery at the end of the 3-minute cooking period, remove fruit from liquid, then continue to heat the water-sugar mixture until it is thicker and somewhat syrupy. Pour the liquid over the fruit for serving.
7. Record total working time: _____ minutes.

Prunes—Soaked Overnight

Prunes, per person	1	1
Water to cover fruit—approximately	1 1/2 cups	375 ml
Sugar—adjust as necessary	1/4 cup	50 ml
Lemon, optional, thin slices	2	2

1. Put soaked fruit and water in a saucepan. Cover saucepan with a tight-fitting lid. Simmer, 185°–200°F (85°–90°C), fruit for 30 minutes. Add more hot water as needed.
2. Remove cover from saucepan. Add sugar, if used.
3. Simmer in an uncovered saucepan for 3 minutes after sugar has been added. (A thin slice of lemon may be added to prunes at the same time as the sugar is added.)
4. If the liquid on the fruit is watery at the end of the 3-minute cooking period, remove fruit from liquid; continue to heat the water-sugar mixture until it is thicker and somewhat syrupy. Pour the liquid over the fruit for serving.
5. Record total working time:_____ minutes.

CHARACTERISTICS OF HIGH QUALITY PRUNES

Appearance: Intact, plump, not deeply wrinkled.
Tenderness: *Skins:* soft, little resistance to bite. *Pulp:* easily removed from pit; smooth, soft, no resistance to bite.
Flavor: Typical; lemon juice may be used to mask sweetness but neither sweetness or lemon flavor should dominate.

OBSERVATIONS ON FRUIT

Fruit	Variety	Color and Appearance	Texture and/or Tenderness	Flavor
Raw apples				

Apple Variety	Treatment	Color and appearance	Other Comments
	Not treated		
	Ascorbic acid treated		
	Not treated		
	Ascorbic acid treated		
	Not treated		
	Ascorbic acid treated		
	Not treated		
	Ascorbic acid treated		

OBSERVATIONS ON FRUIT (Continued)

Fruit	Variety	Color and Appearance	Texture and/or Tenderness	Flavor
Apple sauce				
Coddled apples				
Baked apples				

OBSERVATIONS ON FRUIT (Continued)

Fruit	Treatment	Color and Appearance	Texture and/or Tenderness	Flavor
Prunes	Soaked overnight			
	Soaked in hot water 20 min.			
Cranberry sauce	Cooked in water			
	Cooked in sugar syrup			
Cranberry jelly				

REVIEW QUESTIONS

Questions Applying to Both Fruits and Vegetables

1. Define each of the following terms and discuss its importance in cooking fruits and/or vegetables:
   a. Protopectin.
   b. Hemicellulose.
   c. Cellulose.
   d. Pectin.
   e. Calcium pectate.
2. a. List four pigments that occur naturally in fruits and vegetables.
   b. Cite examples of a fruit and vegetable containing each of the four pigments.
   c. Describe the action of each of the following agents on each of the four pigments:
      (1) Acid.
      (2) Alkali (base).
      (3) Excessive heat.
      (4) Iron.
   d. Name some specific agents in c–1 and c–2.
3. a. What is the role of pectic substances in raw fruits and vegetables?
   b. What is the effect of acid on pectic substances?
   c. What is the effect of alkali on pectic substances?
4. Explain each of the evaluations in the evaluation sheet on the following page.

Questions Applying to Vegetable Only

1. Define each of the following terms and discuss its importance in cooking vegetables:
   a. Oxalic acid.
   b. Solanin.
   c. Sinigren.
   d. Allyl sulfide.
   e. Lignocellulose.
   f. Plant acid.
2. What determines whether a vegetable is cooked with the lid on or the lid off? Discuss.
3. Discuss the relationship of volume of water used in cooking and nutrient value of a cooked vegetable.
4. The famous French chef, Escoffier, in his recipe for *Choux Rouges a la Flamande* (Flamande Red Cabbage), adds a little vinegar and four peeled and quartered cooking apples. Why are these two items used in preparing this dish?
5. a. Describe the effect of storage temperature on sugar and starch in certain vegetables.
   b. What difficulties might storage temperature cause in cooking potatoes?

Questions Applying to Fruits Only

1. Define each of the following terms and discuss its importance in cooking fruits:
   a. Osmosis.
   b. Enzymatic browning.
   c. Organic acids.
   d. Dehydrated fruits.
   e. Gel.
2. a. Why must dehydrated fruits be soaked in water before cooking?
   b. What would happen if dehydrated fruits were cooked in a concentrated sugar solution?
3. a. List some fruits which turn brown when cut slices are exposed to the air.
   b. Describe several ways this browning may be delayed.

EVALUATION OF PRODUCTS

Name: _____

Date: _____

Score System

Points	Quality
7	Excellent
6	Very good
5	Good
4	Medium
3	Fair
2	Poor
1	Very poor

Directions:

1. Place the numerical score in the box in the upper left hand corner.
2. Comments should justify the numerical score. Comments must be brief.
3. Evaluation of the food products must be on an *individual* basis.

Products

Quality Characteristic	Harvard Beets	Baked potato	Broccoli	Prune	Baked Apple
Appearance	3 — Bluish red	4 — Moist; translucent	3 — Olive green	3 — Shriveled	1 — Fell apart
Consistency or Texture	5	4 — Wet; waxy	5	2 — Firm	1 — Soft and mushy
Tenderness	5	5	4 — Too soft	2 — Tough	1 — Too soft
Flavor	4 — Flat; not tart	6	3 — Bitter	4 — Too sweet	5
Overall Eating Quality	3	4	4	2	1

200

Salads

OBJECTIVES

1. To study the roles of salads in meals.
2. To discuss and illustrate the preparation and care of selected greens.
3. To discuss and illustrate the arrangement of salad ingredients for serving.
4. To discuss and illustrate marinades and salad dressings.

PRODUCTS TO BE PREPARED TO ILLUSTRATE PRINCIPLES

Types of Salads

Appetizer	Dinner Accompaniment	Main Course	Dessert
Fruit salad	Cole slaw	Tuna salad	Fresh fruit
Five-bean salad	Tomato (marinated)	Hot potato salad	Frozen fruit
	Caesar salad	Chef's salad	Canned fruit
		Chicken salad	

PRINCIPLES

1. The type of salad will determine the food combination to be used.
   a. *Appetizer* salads are small servings of salad greens or tart fruit which whet rather than satiate the appetite.
   b. *Dinner accompaniment* salads are relatively small servings of vegetable(s) and/or fruits which complement the entree.
   c. *Main course* salads are generous servings of protein, potato, rice, or pasta usually combined with greens or other succulent vegetables. The salad has high satiety value.
   d. *Dessert* salads are medium to small portions of fruit(s).
2. Quality of ingredients:
   a. All ingredients should be edible.
   b. All ingredients should be clean and free from defects (bruises, rotten spots, insects, dirt and sand, and insecticide).
   c. Raw fruits and vegetables should be at their optimum stage of maturity.
   d. All inedible portions should be removed (albedo of citrus fruits, paraffined cucumber skin, for example).

3. Salad greens:
   a. Usually all types of salads are served on an underliner of salad greens.
   b. Salad greens may be used alone or in combination with fruits or other vegetables.
   c. Salad greens are palatable only if clean, crisp, and dry. (Exception—wilted lettuce salad.)
   d. When used as underliners for salads, the salad greens should not extend over the edge of the serving plate.
4. Quality characteristics of salads are dependent on:
   a. Selecting food combinations for contrast in color, texture, and flavor.
   b. Pieces varying in size for contrast and interest.
   c. Poultry and fish pieces being large enough to be identified.
   d. Pasta remaining in discrete pieces (not gummy masses) by rinsing after cooking.
   e. Firm foods (not easily cut with a fork) being in bite-size pieces.
5. Marinades:
   a. May be used to contribute flavor to pasta or other bland-flavored ingredients, firm fruits and vegetables, or meat, fish, and poultry.
   b. The marinade is drained off before ingredients are combined into a salad.
6. Dressings:
   a. Are usually an integral part of the salad.
   b. Flavor of dressing should complement the flavor of the salad.
   c. The type of dressing is determined by how the salad is used in the meal:

Type of Salad	*Suggested Dressings
(1) Appetizer	Tart. Usually of French type—an oil and vinegar dressing.
(2) Dinner Accompaniment	French, mayonnaise, thousand island, Russian, blue cheese, or a special dressing.
(3) Main Course	Any of those listed for dinner accompaniment salads.
(4) Dessert	Mayonnaise or cooked dressings blended with whipped cream. These dressings are usually sweet and rich.

7. A salad must be aesthetically pleasing.

*See pages 212–213 for recipes.

Fruit Salad (Appetizer)

Orange sections or slices	1/2 medium orange
Apple slices, red-skinned apple	1/4 medium apple
Bibb lettuce leaves	3 to 4
French dressing	

1. Pare orange to remove outer white skin with the rind. Either section or cut into slices.
2. Wash and dry the apple. *Do not* remove red skin. Cut the quarter section into 3 or 4 slices: the skin side should not be more than 1/4-inch (0.6 cm) thick. Dip apple slices in orange juice to delay browning.
3. Lettuce leaves should be washed, drained, and dried.
4. Arrange lettuce leaves on suitable serving plate. Alternate orange sections and apple slices on the bed of lettuce.
5. Serve with French dressing.
6. Record total working time: _____ minutes. Yield: 1 serving.

Five-Bean Salad (Appetizer)

*Green beans, whole	1 can	1 can
*Yellow wax beans, cut	1 can	1 can
*Kidney beans	1 can	1 can
*Garbanzo beans	1 can	1 can
*Butter beans	1 can	1 can
Green pepper, large	1	1
Sweet onion, 3 inch (7 cm) diameter	1/2	1/2
Celery, 1/4-inch (0.6 cm) slices	2 cups	250 ml
**Cider vinegar	3 cups	750 ml
Sugar	3 cups	750 ml
Vegetable oil (optional)	1/4 cup	50 ml
Lettuce cups or leaves for each serving		

1. Empty cans of green and yellow wax beans into a collander or strainer. Allow to drain thoroughly. Transfer to a 4-quart (4 L) bowl.
2. Empty kidney beans into a collander or strainer. Carefully rinse under cold, running tap water. Drain thoroughly. Transfer to bowl containing green and wax beans. Follow same procedure for garbanzo and butter beans.
3. Wash green pepper; dry; slice into lengthwise strips. Add to beans.
4. Remove dry skin from onion; wash and dry; slice into rings approximately 1/8-inch (0.3 cm) thick. Separate rings. Add to beans.
5. Wash celery; dry; slice; add to beans.
6. If oil is used, add to beans.
7. In a 2-quart (2 L) saucepan combine vinegar and sugar; bring to a boil. Pour over vegetables.
8. Lightly toss vegetables with two forks. Do this several times as the mixture cools.
9. Cover the bowl; refrigerate at least 4 hours before serving. The salad will be more flavorful if it can marinate 24 hours before serving.
10. To serve: wash, drain and dry lettuce; place on serving plate. Drain bean mixture; arrange on lettuce; 1/2 cup (125 ml) approximate serving portion. No salad dressing is needed.
11. Record total working time: _____ minutes. Yield: 16–20 servings.

*Approximate can size = 1 pound (454 grams).
**If vinegar has a *very* tart flavor, 1/2 cup (125 ml) water can be added.

Tomato Salad—Marinated (Dinner Accompaniment)

Tomatoes, medium large	2	2
French dressing (temporary emulsion)	1/2 cup	125 ml
Parsley, finely minced	1 tablespoon	15 ml
Chives, finely minced	1/2 teaspoon	2 ml
Lettuce cups or leaves	4	4

1. Wash tomatoes; skin by impaling on fork through the core and dipping tomato into boiling water for 5–10 seconds. Plunge into cold water. Slice tomatoes 3/8–inch (1 cm) thick. Arrange in single layer so dressing can be spooned over each slice.
2. Wash parsley; dry; finely mince using scissors. Wash chives; dry; finely mince. Combine parsley and chives with French dressing; allow to stand 5 minutes. Spoon over tomatoes. Refrigerate 1 hour before serving.
3. Wash lettuce; remove excess moisture; place on serving plate.
4. Drain excess dressing from tomato slices before serving on lettuce.
5. Record total working time: _____ minutes. Yield: 4 servings.

Cole Slaw (Dinner Accompaniment)

*Cabbage, green	2 cups	500 ml
Dairy sour cream	1/2 cup	125 ml
Cider vinegar	2 tablespoons	30 ml
Sugar	2 teaspoons	10 ml
Salt	few grains	few grains

1. Wash, dry cabbage; shred into thin, long shreds. Width of shred should not be more than 1/16–inch (0.2 cm). Shreds should be approximately 2 inches (5 cm) in length.
2. Combine the sour cream, vinegar, and sugar.
3. Toss the dressing *lightly* with the shredded cabbage.
4. Serve on a lettuce leaf, if desired.
5. Record total working time:_____ minutes. Yield: 2 servings.

*When green cabbage is not available, 1–2 tablespoons (15–30 ml) shredded carrot or thin slivers of green pepper can be added to provide color to the salad. A mixture of 3 parts green cabbage and 1 part red cabbage may also be used for color contrast.

Caesar Salad (Dinner Accompaniment)

*Salad greens	1 quart	1 L
Seasoned croutons	1 cup	250 ml
Salad oil	1/4 cup	50 ml
Worcestershire sauce	1/2 teaspoon	2 ml
Lemon juice	2 tablespoons	30 ml
Black pepper, freshly ground	few grains	few grains
Raw egg	1	1
Blue cheese or Roquefort, crumbled	1 ounce	30 g

1. Wash and dry salad greens. Break into bite-size pieces; place in an appropriate size bowl.
2. Add the lemon juice, pepper, and Worcestershire sauce to the 1/4 cup (50 ml) salad oil.
3. Pour oil mixture over salad greens; add about half of the croutons; toss *lightly*.
4. Add the whole raw egg and toss lightly to blend. (Do not use egg shell.)
5. Crumble the blue cheese over the top. Add the last portion of croutons.
6. Serve *cold*.
7. Record total working time: _____ minutes. Yield: 4–6 servings.

*Romaine used by itself is traditional. If romaine is unavailable, use a combination of head lettuce, Bibb lettuce and endive.

Seasoned Croutons*

Bread cubes	1 cup	250 ml
Salad oil (olive oil will give distinctive flavor)	1 tablespoon	15 ml
Garlic clove, small	1	1

1. Cut bread into 3/8-inch (1 cm) cubes. Arrange cubes in single layer on baking pan. Brown in a 375°F (190°C) oven.
2. Pour garlic flavored oil over croutons. Toss well.
3. Garlic flavored oil is prepared by allowing a clove of garlic to soak overnight in the oil. Remove garlic clove before using the oil.

*Commercial seasoned croutons may be used as purchased.

Chef's Salad (Main Course)

*Salad greens	1 1/2 cups	375 ml
Swiss cheese	2 ounces	60 g
Brick cheese	1 ounce	30 g
Boiled ham	2 ounces	60 g
Egg, hard cooked	1	1
French dressing	2 tablespoons	30 ml
Lettuce cups or leaves		

1. Start egg to hard cook. (See page 120.)
2. Wash and remove excess water from salad greens. Tear endive, spinach and romaine into bite size pieces.
3. Use the lettuce cups or larger leaves as underliners in the salad bowl.
4. In a small bowl, *lightly* toss together the greens with the French dressing.
5. Place greens in salad bowl, slightly mounding them toward center of bowl.
6. Cut cheese into lengthwise strips, 3/8-inch X 1/8-inch (1 cm X 0.3 cm). Cut ham into lengthwise strips, 1/4-inch X 1/4-inch (0.6 cm X 0.6 cm). Cut egg lengthwise into quarters. Arrange cheeses, ham and hard cooked egg on top of greens.
7. Serve with additional French dressing as desired.
8. Record total working time:_____ minutes. Yield: 1 serving.

*Use a combination of head lettuce chunks, endive, spinach, and romaine.

Hot Potato Salad (Main Course)

Potatoes, waxy variety, medium size	4	4
Salt	1/2 teaspoon	3 ml
Pepper, white	few grains	few grains
Bacon slices	8	8
Eggs, hard cooked	4	4
Green onions	4	4
Bacon fat	2 tablespoons	30 ml
Vinegar, cider	1/2 cup	125 ml

1. Wash potatoes. Pare and cut into 1-inch (2.5 cm) cubes. Cook until tender.
2. Start egg to hard cook. (See page 120.)
3. Cut bacon into 1-inch (2.5 cm) pieces; place in cold fry pan. Cook at low heat, 300°F (150°C) in an electric fry pan, until bacon is crisp. Remove bacon pieces; measure drippings; return 2 tablespoons (30 ml) to fry pan.
4. When potatoes are cool enough to handle (but not cold) cut into pieces approximately 1/4-inch X 1 inch (0.6 cm X 2.5 cm).
5. Remove roots from green onions; wash, dry and finely chop.
6. Add the vinegar to the drippings; heat quickly to boiling. Add potatoes, green onions, seasonings, and sliced hard-cooked eggs. (Reserve several slices of eggs for garnish, if desired.) *Lightly* toss ingredients together using forks. Add the pieces of bacon. Garnish and serve. (This can be served from electric fry pan to keep the salad hot.)
7. Record total working time:_____ minutes. Yield: 4 servings.

Tuna Salad (Main Course)

Tuna, "Whole meat" style	1 cup	250 ml
Cucumber	1/2 cup	125 ml
Celery	1/2 cup	125 ml
Egg, hard cooked	1	1
Mayonnaise dressing	1/2 cup	125 ml
Lettuce cups or leaves	2	2

1. Start egg to hard cook. (See page 120.)
2. Leave tuna fish in *large* chunks. Drain off excess oil; place tuna in a small bowl.
3. Wash and dry celery and cucumber; dice celery into 1/4-inch (0.6 cm) dice; slice cucumber into 1/8-inch (0.3 cm) slices. Add mayonnaise, celery and cucumber to tuna; toss *lightly* together using two forks. Do *not* overwork.
4. Place lettuce on an appropriate size plate; place tuna mixture into lettuce cup.
5. Cut hard-cooked egg into quarters lengthwise. Use for garnish.
6. Serve with additional mayonnaise as desired.
7. Record total working time:_____minutes. Yield: 2 servings.

Chicken Salad (Main Course)

Chicken, cooked	1 cup	250	ml
Salt	1/16 teaspoon	0.2	ml
Celery	1/2 cup	125	ml
Pineapple chunks, well drained	1/2 cup	125	ml
Ripe olives, pitted	6	6	
Slivered almonds, toasted	2 tablespoons	30	ml
Mayonnaise	1/4 cup	50	ml
Lettuce cups or leaves	2	2	

1. Place almonds in a heavy fry pan; place pan over low heat; stir nuts occasionally for even browning. Cool nuts before adding to other ingredients. Use to garnish salad.
2. Cut chicken into 3/4-inch (2 cm) cubes. Place chicken in a small bowl. Add salt. Use two forks to *lightly* toss chicken to distribute salt. Do not overwork.
3. Cut each pineapple chunk into 2 or 3 pieces. Add to chicken.
4. Wash and drain celery; cut into 1/4-inch (0.6 cm) dice. Add to chicken.
5. Halve or quarter olives. Add olives and mayonnaise to chicken. Use two forks to *lightly* toss ingredients together. Do *not* overwork.
6. Wash lettuce; drain thoroughly. Arrange on appropriate size plates.
7. Serve half of chicken mixture in each lettuce cup. Garnish with toasted almonds.
8. Serve with additional mayonnaise as desired.
9. Record total working time:_____minutes. Yield: 2 servings.

Fresh Fruit Salad (Dessert)

Orange sections or slices	1/3 medium orange
Pineapple, fresh	3 or 4 chunks or pieces
Banana	4 to 5 slices
Grapes, dark skinned preferred	3 to 5 seeded
Boston or Bibb lettuce leaves	1 to 4
Honey-lemon-oil dressing	

1. Pare orange to remove outer white skin with the rind. Either section or cut into slices.
2. Remove heavy skin from a 1/2-inch (1.3 cm) slice of fresh pineapple. Cut slice in half. Remove core. Cut a half slice into several pieces.
3. Cut bananas into 1/4–3/8-inch (0.6–1 cm) slices. The banana could first be scored with a fork, if desired. Dip banana slices in orange juice to delay browning.
4. Wash and dry grapes; cut in half if large; remove any seeds that may be present.
5. Lettuce leaves should be washed, drained, and dried. Put lettuce leaves on serving plate.
6. Arrange fruit casually on lettuce; avoid a "worked-over" appearance. Serve with Honey-Lemon-Oil Dressing (page 213).
7. Record total working time: _____ minutes. Yield: 1 serving.

Canned Fruit Salad (Dessert)

Pineapple chunks	2 cups	500 ml
Apricot halves	8-10	8-10
Maraschino cherries	8	8
Marshmallows, large	8	8
Whipping cream	1/2 cup	125 ml
*Mayonnaise dressing	1/2 cup	125 ml
Slivered almonds, toasted	2 tablespoons	30 ml
Boston or Bibb lettuce leaves for 4 servings		

1. Thoroughly drain the canned fruits. Cut the apricot halves into two or three slices. Cut the maraschino cherries into halves. Cut the marshmallows into quarters.
2. Whip the cream. Blend with the mayonnaise. Use approximately 1/2 cup (125 ml) of the blended dressing to mix *lightly* with the fruit. *Do not* overblend so fruit becomes mushy. This mixture should stand at least 1 hour before serving for better blending of flavors.
3. Lettuce leaves should be washed, drained, and, if necessary, dried.
4. Put lettuce leaves on serving plate. Add fruit mixture. Sprinkle with toasted, slivered almonds. Serve with remaining portion of whipped cream dressing.
5. Record total working time: _____ minutes. Yield: 4 servings.

*Fruit Salad Dressing, page 213, can be substituted for the mayonnaise to enhance fruity flavor of the salad.

Frozen Fruit Salad (Dessert)

Apricot halves or peach slices, canned	1 1/2 cups	375 ml
Pineapple chunks, canned	1 cup	250 ml
*White grapes, canned	3/4 cup	175 ml
Cream cheese, 3 ounce (approx. 90 g) package	1	1
Lemon juice	1 tablespoon	15 ml
Sugar	1 tablespoon	15 ml
Whipping cream	1/2 cup	125 ml
Mayonnaise	1/2 cup	125 ml
Mint sprigs (fresh), if desired		

1. Thoroughly drain all canned fruits; apricot halves may be cut into thirds; peach slices may be cut in half; pineapple chunks may be cut into thirds.
2. In a 2-quart (2 L) bowl, blend the cream cheese with the lemon juice and sugar. Blend until smooth.
3. Add the mayonnaise dressing gradually to the cheese mixture, blending after each addition to keep the mixture smooth.
4. Whip the cream: add to the cream cheese-mayonnaise mixture. *Do not overblend.*
5. Add the drained fruits. Blend. Pour mixture into refrigerator trays for freezing. Freeze until firm (approximately 2–3 hours).
6. For serving, slice into serving portions. Place a portion on washed, drained, and dried lettuce leaves. Garnish with a sprig of mint, if desired.
7. Record total working time: _____ minutes. Yield: 9 servings.

*Minted pears or green maraschino cherries could be substituted for the grapes.

CHARACTERISTICS OF HIGH QUALITY SALADS

Appearance: Greens—crisp, moist (not wet). Fruits, vegetables, and meat—pieces large enough to be identified. Aesthetically pleasing, simple, and casual.
Color: Pleasing selection of contrasting colors *or* a blend of monochromatic colors.
Texture: Greens—firm and crisp. Fruits, vegetables, and meat—firm; all pieces in a combination salad must be of compatible texture. Pasta—soft and free of any gumminess.
Tenderness: Greens—firm crisp. Fruits, vegetables, meat, and pasta—little resistance to bite. Skins of fruits and vegetables (apple, tomato, cucumber) must be tender.
*Ease of eating:** Pieces of firm, raw vegetables (carrots, cauliflower, and so on) of a size to be easily managed with a fork; connective membranes of citrus fruit removed or cut for ease in eating.
Flavor: Appropriate for use of salad; balanced, well blended.

*This characteristic is important enough in salads to be evaluated along with the other characteristics.

REVIEW QUESTIONS

1. List the four types of salads as identified with their place in the meal. Briefly describe each type.
2. a. List the four requirements for quality of ingredients.
   b. List factors to consider in care and use of salad greens.
   c. Why should salad greens be torn rather than cut?
   d. Why must salad greens be dry when used?
   e. Why should cleaned salad greens be refrigerated in a tightly closed container?
3. a. List several factors to be considered in arranging an attractive salad.
   b. Discuss several ways in which contrast (variety) might be obtained in a salad.
4. What are marinades and how are they used?
5. Discuss factors to consider when deciding what type of salad dressing to use.

Salad Dressings

OBJECTIVES

1. To discuss and review the principles of emulsion formation.
2. To illustrate the preparation of a food emulsion.
3. To introduce the student to the principles of reforming "broken" emulsions.
4. To discuss composition of types of dressings used in salad preparation.
5. To emphasize the bacteriological implications in using mayonnaise dressing or salad dressings.
6. To review principles of starch-egg cookery.

PRODUCTS TO BE PREPARED TO ILLUSTRATE PRINCIPLES

Mayonnaise dressing
French dressing (optional)

PRINCIPLES

1. Emulsions may be either *temporary* or *permanent* depending on stability.
2. Stability of an emulsion system is dependent on particle size and the presence of an emulsifier.
3. Temperature of ingredients determines the ease of forming an emulsion.
4. Temperature of storage in part determines the stability of the emulsion.
5. A "broken" emulsion can be re-emulsified because:
   a. Adding the broken emulsion to an egg yolk is similar to adding oil to egg yolk as in the original production.
   b. By adding the broken emulsion to water or vinegar, the liquid dilutes the emulsifier present in the broken emulsion so the emulsifier can again function.
6. The term *salad dressing* is extremely broad: it can apply to any type of dressing used on a salad. Specific Standards of Identity which define the composition and ingredients used are found in the Code of Federal Regulations: Title 21-, Part 169, dated April 1, 1983.

Mayonnaise Dressing (Permanent Emulsion)

Egg yolk	1	1
Salt	1/4 teaspoon	1 ml
Cayenne	few grains	few grains
Mustard, dry	1/2 teaspoon	2 ml
Sugar	1/2 teaspoon	2 ml
*Vinegar	2 tablespoons	30 ml
Vegetable oil	1 cup	250 ml

1. Put the egg yolk in a small, deep bowl; add salt, cayenne, mustard, and sugar; mix.
2. Mix in 1 tablespoon (15 ml) vinegar.
3. Add 1–2 drops of oil and beat vigorously, using rotary beater or electric mixer. Continue adding the oil a few drops at a time, beating vigorously after each addition until about 1/4 cup (50 ml) of oil has been used.*
4. Beat in the remaining oil; add 1–2 tablespoons (15–30 ml) at a time; beat in remaining vinegar when the mixture becomes quite thick (about half the oil has been added).
5. Record total working time: _____ minutes.

*Amount of oil added as one addition should never be more than half the volume of the emulsion already formed.

Re-emulsification of Mayonnaise

The emulsion in mayonnaise may break, permitting the oil and water to separate into layers. Freezing or storage at too low a temperature will cause this breakdown. Mayonnaise which is too thick may separate on standing. The emulsion may be restored by the following procedure:

1. Place one egg yolk* in a small, deep bowl; beat lightly with rotary beater.
2. Add the broken mayonnaise 1–2 teaspoons (5–10 ml) at a time; use rotary beater or electric mixer to beat thoroughly after each addition until the emulsion reforms. Larger amounts of broken emulsion can be added as the emulsion is reformed. (See footnote for mayonnaise dressing.)

*One tablespoon (15 ml) of water or vinegar may be used in place of the egg yolk.

CHARACTERISTICS OF HIGH QUALITY MAYONNAISE DRESSING

Appearance: Shiny; emulsion stable.
Color: Yellow; shade dependent on color of egg yolk and source of acid.
Consistency: Mounds firmly on spoon even when diluted with other ingredients such as whipped cream, chili sauce, catsup, or pickle relish.
Mouth Feel: Somewhat oily.
Flavor: Spices well-blended; slightly tart.

French Dressing (Temporary Emulsion)

Vegetable oil	2/3 cup	150 ml
*Vinegar	1/3 cup	75 ml
Sugar	1 teaspoon	5 ml
Salt	1/4 teaspoon	1 ml
Paprika	1/4 teaspoon	1 ml
Mustard, dry	1/4 teaspoon	1 ml
Cayenne	few grains	few grains

1. Blend together all dry ingredients. Place in a 2-cup (500 ml) container which has a tight closure.
2. Add the vinegar and the vegetable oil. Shake the mixture vigorously before using.
3. Record total working time: _____ minutes. Yield: 1 cup (250 ml).

   *Either white or cider vinegar can be used. Cider vinegar contributes a slightly fruity flavor, but does give a darker color to the dressing. For a fruity flavor, use lemon juice in place of the vinegar.

Honey-Lemon-Oil Dressing (Temporary Emulsion)

Lemon juice	1/4 cup	50 ml
Honey	1/4 cup	50 ml
Salad oil	1/4 cup	50 ml
Celery seed (optional)	1/8 teaspoon	0.5 ml

1. Place all ingredients in a 1-cup (250 ml) container which has a tightly fitting closure.
2. Shake ingredients together vigorously just before serving.
3. Record total working time: _____ minutes. Yield: 3/4 cup (175 ml).

Fruit Salad Dressing (Cooked Starch Based)

Pineapple juice	1/4 cup	50 ml
Orange juice	1/2 cup	125 ml
Lemon juice	2 tablespoons	30 ml
Water	1/4 cup	50 ml
Salt	1/8 teaspoon	0.5 ml
Sugar	1/3 cup	75 ml
Flour	2 tablespoons	30 ml
Egg	1	1
Whipping cream	1/2 cup	125 ml

1. Blend together in a 1 or 1 1/2 quart (1–1.5 L) saucepan the salt, sugar, and flour.
2. Gradually add the fruit juices and water. Stir until all ingredients are evenly blended.
3. Place over heat. Stir constantly; bring to a boil; boil 1 minute. Remove from heat.
4. Blend egg in a 2–3 cup (500–750 ml) bowl.
5. Gradually add hot starch mixture, about 1 tablespoon (15 ml) at a time, to egg; stir after each addition to thoroughly blend. When approximately half the starch has been added to the egg, pour all of egg-starch mixture into remaining starch paste. Blend thoroughly.
6. Return egg-starch mixture to medium heat. Stir constantly until egg is coagulated, about 4–5 minutes. Mixture should be near boiling point, but should *not* boil. Remove from heat.
7. Cool dressing before using on fruit salad.
8. Whip cream just before using dressing. Fold into dressing.
9. Record total working time: _____ minutes. Yield: 2–2 1/2 cups (500–625 ml).

REVIEW QUESTIONS

1. a. What is the difference between a temporary and a permanent emulsion?
   b. Which ingredients function as emulsifying agents in mayonnaise?
   c. List some other ingredients which function as emulsifying agents in salad dressings. (*Note:* Read the ingredient lists on samples of commercial products.)
2. According to Standards of Identity how do mayonnaise and salad dressing differ:
   a. In composition?
   b. In permitted ingredients?

Gelatin

OBJECTIVES

1. To illustrate principles involved in the preparation of gelatin products.
2. To compare quality characteristics of a gelatin prepared from plain, dry gelatin and a commercial gelatin mix.
3. To illustrate and discuss factors that affect the strength of a gelatin gel.
4. To illustrate and discuss factors that affect a gelatin foam.
5. To illustrate and discuss basic ingredients of typical gelatin food products.

PRODUCTS TO BE PREPARED TO ILLUSTRATE PRINCIPLES

Plain jellies	Spanish cream
Gelatin foam	Bavarian creams
Gelatin sponges	Chiffons

PRINCIPLES

1. Dry gelatin particles must be separated before heating by:
   a. Mixing gelatin granules with cold water.
   b. Diluting with other dry ingredients (sugar, acids, and salts, as in the commercial mix.
2. All gelatin granules are "dissolved" in the water by the application of heat to form gelatin sols.
3. Factors that affect transformation of gelatin sols to gels include:
   a. Concentration of gelatin.
   b. Temperature.
   c. Acidity.
   d. Sugar.
   e. Buffer salts.
4. The effect of the five factors listed in Principle 3 are observed as:
   a. Rate of gel formation.
   b. Strength of the gel.
5. Pieces of added food materials that are too large will rupture a gel structure.
6. In formation of gelatin foam, air incorporation increases the volume and decreases intensity of color and flavor.
7. Dissolved gelatin will not retain air for foam formation until it has attained the consistency of raw egg white.
8. A gelatin solution that "sets" prematurely (before whipping or before adding fruit or vegetable pieces) can be re-liquified (by heating) and re-chilled to desired consistency.

PLAIN JELLIES AND GELATIN FOAM

Orange Jelly

Gelatin	1 tablespoon	15 ml
Water	1/3 cup	75 ml
Sugar	1/2 cup	125 ml
Lemon juice, fresh	2 tablespoons	30 ml
Frozen, concentrated orange juice, unsweetened	1/3 cup	75 ml
Water	1 cup	250 ml

1. Allow orange juice to thaw.
2. Place 1/3 cup (75 ml) cold water in the upper part of a double boiler. Sprinkle the gelatin over the top of the water. Allow to stand for 5 minutes.
3. Place the hydrated gelatin over boiling water. Stir until gelatin has dissolved. No particles of gelatin should be seen.
4. Add sugar; stir until dissolved. Add all other ingredients.
*5. Stir until thoroughly blended. Pour half into mold. Chill mold in a pan of chipped ice. When firm, unmold for evaluation.
6. Use the remaining half portion for a gelatin foam as directed below.
7. Record total working time: _____ minutes.

Orange Gelatin Foam

1. Place the remaining half portion of orange jelly in a 1-quart (1 L) glass measuring cup. Measure quantity. Place the glass cup in a pan of chipped ice. Chill until the gelatin has the consistency of raw egg white.
2. Leave the mixture in the glass cup; beat with an electric mixer at high speed until the mixture is light and holds up in soft peaks. Measure quantity of foam. Foam can be left to become firm in glass cup or may be transferred to a mold for gelatin.*
3. Compare color and flavor of the jelly product with color and flavor of the foam product. Compare volume of jelly product with volume of foam product.
4. Record total working time: _____ minutes.

Orange Jelly—Commercial Mix Product

Gelatin mix, orange flavor, 3 ounces (approx. 90 g)	1 package	1 package
Water	2 cups	500 ml

1. Prepare by directions on package.
*2. Dissolved gelatin can be molded as just plain jelly, or a comparison of jelly and foam as outlined above may be followed.
3. Record total working time: _____ minutes.

*Small ring molds are preferred for most of the gelatin products since the products can be chilled rapidly. Individual molds can be used, but are time consuming to fill and to wash and dry.
A small ring mold holds approximately 2 cups (500 ml).
An individual mold contains approximately 1/3 cup (75 ml).

Tomato Aspic

Gelatin	1 tablespoon	15 ml
Tomato juice	1 3/4 cups	425 ml
Salt	1/4 teaspoon	1 ml
Sugar	1/2 teaspoon	2 ml
Worcestershire sauce	1/2 teaspoon	2 ml
Tabasco sauce	1-2 drops	1-2 drops
Lemon juice, fresh	2 tablespoons	30 ml

1. Place 1/2 cup (125 ml) of the tomato juice in the upper part of the double boiler. Add the gelatin. Allow to stand 5 minutes.
2. Dissolve the hydrated gelatin over boiling water. Be sure all gelatin is dissolved.
*3. Add remaining ingredients. Stir until all are blended and sugar and salt are dissolved. Pour into mold; chill until firm.
4. Record total working time: _____ minutes.

Perfection Salad

Gelatin	1 tablespoon	15 ml
Sugar	1/4 cup	50 ml
Salt	1/2 teaspoon	2 ml
Water	1 1/4 cup	300 ml
Vinegar	2 tablespoons	30 ml
Lemon juice	1 tablespoon	15 ml
Cabbage	1/2 cup	125 ml
Celery	1 cup	250 ml
Green pepper	1 tablespoon	15 ml
Sweet red pepper or canned pimiento	1 tablespoon	15 ml

1. Mix gelatin, sugar, and salt together in a saucepan. Add 1/2 cup (125 ml) of the water. Place over low heat. Stir constantly until the gelatin is dissolved.
2. Remove from heat. Stir in remaining water, vinegar, and lemon juice.
3. Chill until the consistency of raw egg white.
4. Wash cabbage; use french knife to shred into fine shreds, 1/8-inch wide X 2 inches long (0.3 cm X 5 cm). Wash celery; drain off excess water; cut into 1/4-inch (0.6 cm) dice. Wash green pepper; dry; cut into 1/4-inch (0.6 cm) dice. If fresh, sweet red pepper is used, follow directions for green pepper; or cut pimiento into thin strips. Fold prepared vegetables into the gelatin when it has consistency of raw egg white.
*5. Spoon into a 2-cup (500 ml) mold. Chill until firm.
6. Record total working time: _____ minutes.

*See Note bottom page 216.

Reception Salad

Lime gelatin dessert mix, 3 ounces (approx. 90 g)	1 package	1 package
Plain gelatin	1 teaspoon	5 ml
Water	3/4 cup	175 ml
Canned pear liquid	3/4 cup	175 ml
Salt	1/2 teaspoon	2 ml
Canned pear halves	4–5	4–5
Cottage cheese	3/4 cup	175 ml
Ginger	1/2 teaspoon	2 ml
Lemon juice	1 tablespoon	15 ml
Red-skinned apple, unpeeled	1	1

1. Bring to a boil 3/4 cup (175 ml) water. Add to the lime gelatin mixed with the plain gelatin. Stir until all gelatin is dissolved.
2. Add the pear syrup, salt, lemon juice, and mix.
3. Pour one-third gelatin mixture into the bottom of a 1-quart (1 L) ring mold. Allow to chill until the gelatin is the consistency of raw egg white. Arrange alternate slices of apples and pears so the fruit is perpendicular to the bottom of the mold (see Steps 4 and 5). Fruit slices must not extend above the rim of the mold.
4. Wash and dry the apple. *Do not* peel. Cut the apple into quarters, lengthwise. Core. Cut each quarter into lengthwise wedges so each wedge is approximately 1/4-inch (0.6 cm) wide on the skin side. Red skin of apples will be at the outside of the mold.
5. Cut each pear half into lengthwise slices approximately 1/2-inch (1.3 cm) wide on the outside.
6. Chill remaining gelatin mixture until it is the consistency of raw egg white. Whip until the mixture holds in soft peaks.
7. Cream the cottage cheese, using an electric mixer; add ginger; blend thoroughly.
8. Fold cheese mixture into whipped gelatin. Pour cheese-gelatin foam over the fruit. Chill until gelatin is firm.
9. Record total working time: _____ minutes.

REVIEW QUESTIONS

1. What steps are necessary to "dissolve" gelatin? (How is the gelatin sol formed?)
2. Explain why plain gelatin must be soaked in cold water while a commercial gelatin mix can be added directly to boiling water.
3. a. Define gelatin.
   b. In the preparation of gelatin desserts, what causes gelation to take place?
   c. In the case of gelatin the sol-gel transformation is said to be reversible. What is meant by this? What is the practical importance of this?
4. What is the effect of each of the following ingredients on the rate of gel formation and the strength of the resulting gel?
   a. Sugar.
   b. Acid.
   c. Buffer salts.
5. In making Perfection Salad, what would happen if the pieces of vegetable were cut too coarsely?
6. a. Discuss the essential requirement for the formation of a stable gelatin foam.
   b. Compare the color and flavor of a plain jelly and a gelatin foam, both made from the same mix.
7. a. What is the common ingredient in the following products?
   b. What ingredient(s) or treatment identifies each product?
      (1) Gelatin jelly.
      (2) Gelatin foam.
      (3) Lemon sponge.
      (4) Spanish cream.
      (5) Bavarian cream.
      (6) Chiffons.

Beverages

OBJECTIVES

1. To illustrate selected factors that may affect the quality characteristics of beverages:
   a. Method of commercial processing.
   b. Method of preparation of beverage.

PRODUCTS TO BE PREPARED TO ILLUSTRATE PRINCIPLES

Steeped coffee
Percolated coffee
Dripped coffee
Vacuum coffee
Green tea
Black tea
Iced tea (black)
Chocolate
Cocoa

PRINCIPLES

1. Some beverages such as tea and coffee are composed of water-soluble constituents extracted from certain leaves, berries, or roots.
   a. Solubility of the beverage components is dependent on:
      (1) Temperature of water.
      (2) Length of steeping period.
      (3) Effect of acid on the solubility of tannin.
   b. Quality characteristics of tea and coffee are dependent on:
      (1) Volatile flavoring constituents.
      (2) Polyphenols (tannins).
      (3) Caffeine.
      (4) Type of water used for extraction of soluble constituents.
      (5) Individual consumer standards of acceptability.
   c. Commercial processing of the base ingredient (tea leaves or coffee berries) influences the following:
      (1) Color of beverage.
      (2) Volatile flavoring constituents developed.
      (3) Solubility of polyphenols (tannins).
      (4) Presence of caffeine (decaffeinated coffee).
   d. Nutrient content of steeped infusion is negligible.

2. For some beverages the base ingredient becomes an integral part of the beverage as in chocolate and cocoa. For Standards of Identity see Code of Federal Regulations: Title 21– part 163 dated April 1, 1983.
   a. Chocolate contains not less than 50% cacao fat.
   b. Cocoa may contain variable amounts of cacao fat. "Breakfast" cocoa may contain not less than 22% cacao fat.
   c. Special alkalizing treatment (Dutch Process) produces a redder colored product with slightly milder flavor.
   d. Chocolate and cocoa contain starch, which must be gelatinized to contribute to the stability of the beverage.
   e. Fluid milk or dried milk solids and water are the usual liquids used in preparing the beverage: milk becomes an integral component of these beverages (chocolate, cocoa).
   f. Coagulation of heat-coagulable proteins (lactalbumin, lactoglobulin) may result in an undesirable film on the surface of the beverage.
   g. Nutrient content is relatively high—dependent on:
      (1) Use of chocolate or cocoa.
      (2) Type and amount of milk used.
3. Effect of acids on solubility of polyphenols in preparation of iced tea.

STANDARD CAFFEINE CONTENT VALUES*

Coffee (5 ounces)	mg
Brewed from ground roasted	80
Instant	60
Decaffeinated	3

Tea (5 ounces)	
Brewed from leaf or bag	40
Instant	30

Cocoa and Chocolate	
Cocoa, hot chocolate (5 ounces)	4
Chocolate milk (8 ounces)	5

*Food Technology 37: (No. 9), 32-39 (1983).

Steeped Coffee

1. Add ground coffee to water. Stir until coffee grounds are wetted.
2. Heat to 200°F (94°C). Hold at this temperature for 3–5 minutes.
3. Beverage may be poured into a preheated pot for serving.
4. Use only half of the amount made for steeped coffee and use the remainder for clarified steeped coffee as directed below.
5. Record total working time: _____ minutes.

Clarified Steeped Coffee

1. Use 2 tablespoons (30 ml) egg white with 2 cups (500 ml) of coffee from the steeped coffee.
2. Beat the egg white until it is foamy. Stir it into the coffee beverage. Bring the beverage up to the boiling point and boil for about 1 minute. Set the pot off the heat to allow the grounds to settle. The egg white traps particles of coffee grounds as the egg white coagulates.
3. Compare the two steeped beverage for clarity and flavor.
4. Record total working time: _____ minutes.

COFFEE BEVERAGES

	U.S.A.			Metric	
	Amount of Ground Coffee			Amount of Ground Coffee	
Water (8 oz cup)	Recommended*	Laboratory	Water	Recommended*	Laboratory
3 cups	1/2 cup	1/4 cup plus 2 tablespoons	0.75 L	125 ml	80 ml
4 1/2 cups	3/4 cup	1/2 cup plus 1 tablespoon	1.12 L	175 ml	140 ml
6 cups	1 cup	3/4 cup	1.50 L	250 ml	175 ml

*Ratio of ground coffee to water recommended by The Coffee Brewing-Institute, Inc.

Method of Preparation	Type of Grind
Steeping	Regular
Percolate	Regular
Drip or ADC	Drip or ADC
Vacuum	Drip or fine

Recommendation: Do not brew less than two thirds of the capacity of the coffee-maker for best results from the coffeemaker.

Percolated Coffee

1. Put water into percolator pot.
2. Place ground coffee in the basket section of the percolator.
3. Heat: keep the water percolating moderately for 5 minutes if heating over a gas or electric burner. *Or* when using an electric percolator, allow to heat until the signal light is lighted or until the percolating process stops.*
4. Record total working time: _____ minutes.

*Most electric percolators *must not* be placed in water as they are washed. Their electric units must be kept *out* of the water. Some new models, however, do have immersible electric units. *Always check* to see which type of electric unit is in the coffeemaker you have used.

Filtered Coffee—Drip Process*

1. Put ground coffee in basket part of dripolator. Fit basket into lower section. Put upper section (for water) in position.
2. Bring water to an active boil, 212°F (100°C). Use saucepan.
3. Pour *boiling* water into upper section of dripolator. Have the dripolator sitting near a warm burner.
4. After water has filtered through the coffee grounds, heat the beverage to 200°F (94°C) for serving.
5. Record total working time:_____ minutes.

*Principles of beverage extraction also apply in Automatic Coffee Makers.

Filtered Coffee—Vacuum Process

1. Put the water in the lower section of the coffeemaker.
2. Adjust closure for the upper part of the coffeemaker; add the ground coffee; firmly fit the upper section onto the lower section of the coffeemaker.
3. Heat until water is forced up into the ground coffee.
4. Remove coffeemaker fromheat; as the coffeemaker cools, the coffee beverage should filter into the lower section of the coffeemaker.
5. When the beverage has filtered into the lower section, remove the upper section.
6. Reheat beverage to 200°F (94°C), if necessary, for serving.
7. Record total working time: _____ minutes.

Instant Coffee

Coffee, instant—3–4 tablespoons (45–60 ml)
Water—4 cups (1 L)

1. Put instant coffee into an enamel or heat resistant glass coffeepot.
2. Add water.
3. Heat to 200°F (94°C). Hold at this temperature for 5 minutes.
4. Serve.
5. Record total working time: _____ minutes.

Freeze-Dried Coffee

Coffee, freeze dried—2–3 tablespoons (30–45 ml)
Water—4 cups (1 L)

1. Put the freeze dried coffee into a preheated coffeepot.
2. Bring the water to a boil in a saucepan and add to the coffee.
3. Allow to set over a warm burner for 5 minutes before serving (200°F or 94°C).
4. Record total working time:_____ minutes.

CHARACTERISTICS OF HIGH QUALITY COFFEE BEVERAGES

Appearance: Clear, bright.
Aroma: Pleasingly fragrant.
Flavor: Fresh coffee flavor with no bitterness.

TEA BEVERAGES

Green or Black Tea

Tea bag—1 (2.2 grams or 0.08 ounce) or 3/4–1 teaspoon (3–5 ml)
Water—1 cup (250 ml)

1. Preheat teapot by filling with boiling water. Allow to stand while bringing *fresh* water to a boil.
2. Discard water from teapot. Place tea bag in the preheated pot.
3. Add the freshly boiling water. Keep the teapot on a warm burner (but *not* over direct heat). Allow tea to steep for 3 minutes.
4. Serve in white-lined cups when comparing beverages prepared from several types of tea.
5. Record total working time: _____ minutes.

Iced Tea

Tea	3 teaspoons	6.6	g
or	3 bags	3	bags
Water, boiling	2 cups	500	ml
Chipped ice	2 cups	500	ml
Lemon juice	2 teaspoons	10	ml

1. Preheat pint- or quart-size (500 ml–1 L) glass measuring cup with boiling water.
2. Discard water from cup. Put the tea bags in the preheated cup.
3. Add freshly boiling water. Keep cup warm. Allow to steep for 8 minutes.
4. Place 1/2 cup (125 ml) chipped ice into each of 4 glasses.
5. Pour an equal amount of the hot tea beverage into each of the glasses.
6. Add 1 teaspoon (5 ml) lemon juice into each of 2 glasses*
7. Record total working time: _____ minutes.

*If beverage is cloudy, more lemon juice may be added.

CHARACTERISTICS OF HIGH QUALITY TEA BEVERAGES

Appearance: Clear, bright.
Color: Depth of color somewhat dependent on time of steeping. Green tea—yellow-green. Black tea—amber.
Flavor: Distinctive of type—green tea will be somewhat more bitter than black tea.

CHOCOLATE AND COCOA BEVERAGES

Chocolate

Chocolate	1/4 square (1/4 ounce)	1/4	square (7 g)
Sugar	1 tablespoon	15	mil
Water	1/4 cup	50	ml
Milk	1 cup	250	ml
Vanilla	1/8 teaspoon	0.5	ml

1. Combine water, chocolate, and sugar in smallest size saucepan. Heat to boiling with constant stirring. Continue boiling (with stirring) until a smooth paste forms. *Caution: do not* scorch mixture as it reaches consistency of paste.
2. Add milk; heat to 200°F (94°C); add vanilla; serve.
3. Record total working time:_____ minutes.

Cocoa

Cocoa	1 tablespoon	15	ml
Sugar	1 tablespoon	15	ml
Water	1/4 cup	50	ml
Milk	1 cup	250	ml
Vanilla	1/8 teaspoon	0.5	ml

1. Mix together cocoa and sugar in smallest size saucepan; add water; blend.
2. Heat to boiling with constant stirring. Continue boiling (with stirring) until smooth paste forms. *Do not* allow mixture to scorch as it reaches consistency of paste.
3. Add milk; heat to 200°F (94°C); add vanilla; serve.
4. Record total working time:_____ minutes.

CHARACTERISTICS OF HIGH QUALITY CHOCOLATE OR COCOA BEVERAGES

Appearance: Surface is free from milk scum or a layer of fat.
Consistency: Smooth, even consistency of thin cream.
Flavor: Definite, well-blended chocolate flavor; vanilla should be well blended with the chocolate to enhance the chocolate flavor.

REVIEW QUESTIONS

General
1. Discuss the effect of brewing time and temperature of water on extraction of soluble constituents in making coffee and tea.
2. Discuss the use of hard water in making coffee and tea.
3. List the factors which will determine the color, aroma, and flavor of coffee and tea.
4. Discuss the nutrient content of:
   a. Coffee.
   b. Tea.
   c. Hot chocolate.

Coffee
1. Discuss the principles which apply to brewing coffee by each of the three basic methods.
2. Why are coffee beans roasted before grinding?
3. Discuss the importance of using the correct grind of coffee for each method.
4. a. Discuss the staling of coffee.
   b. What is the relationship of packaging of coffee to staling?

Tea
1. What factors determine the grade of tea?
2. a. List the principal types of tea.
   b. Discuss the differences in manufacture of the different types.
   c. How do these differences in methods of manufacture affect the beverage as served?
3. Why does too long a brewing period produce a bitter flavor in the beverage?
4. a. What is the effect of adding lemon to tea?
   b. Explain why this happens.

Chocolate and Cocoa
1. Discuss the Standards of Identity as applied to cocoa and chocolate.
2. a. What are the two processes for making cocoa from cacao nibs?
   b. What are the characteristics of cocoa produced by each process?
3. What is accomplished by forming chocolate or cocoa pastes before adding the milk?

Crystallization: Sugar (Candies)

OBJECTIVES

1. To acquaint the student with selected factors that affect crystallization of sugar syrup mixtures:
   a. Concentration of sugar.
   b. Temperature:
      (1) To which sugar syrups are cooked.
      (2) To which sugar syrups may be cooled before beating.
   c. Extent of beating.
   d. Addition of interfering agents:
      (1) Those that cause hydrolysis.
      (2) Those that have "coating" action.
2. To give students opportunity to compare textures of selected crystalline and amorphous candies.

PRODUCTS TO BE PREPARED TO ILLUSTRATE PRINCIPLES

Crystalline products
   Chocolate fudge
   Penuche fudge
   Divinity fudge

Amorphous products
   Caramels
   Peanut brittle
   Lollipops

PRINCIPLES

1. Factors that affect the concentration of sugar in a syrup.
   a. At any given temperature, a certain amount of sugar (sucrose) can be dissolved to make a syrup.
   b. The concentration of sugar in solution becomes greater as the temperature increases.
   c. A solution is said to be supersaturated when the amount of sugar in solution exceeds that theoretically possible at any temperature.
   d. Supersaturation results from cooling a sugar syrup which has been heated to increase the concentration of sugar in the syrup.

2. Factors that affect the crystallization of sugar in a sugar syrup:
    a. When supersaturation occurs, the sugar may *crystallize.*
    b. *Nuclei* must be present for crystallization. Substances that can act as nuclei are:
        (1) A minute crystal of sugar.
        (2) A particle of colloidal dimension.
        (3) A scratch or rough spot on the pan.
    c. Nuclei formation may also be spontaneous within the sugar syrup.
    d. The greater the *degree of supersaturation* the larger the number of crystals formed and the smaller the size of the crystals formed when the cooked, cooled sugar syrup is beaten.
    e. The *viscosity* of a cooked sugar syrup increases with cooling; increased viscosity fosters formation of many small crystals.
    f. *Beating* a cooked, *cooled* sugar syrup fosters the formation of many small crystals.
    g. A cooked sugar syrup beaten at high temperature crystallizes with formation of fewer and larger crystals.
    h. Crystals continue to grow in size in an underbeaten crystalline candy.
3. Effect of other ingredients on sucrose crystallization:
    a. Substances which alter rate of crystallization or size of crystals are called *interfering agents* or *doctoring agents.*
    b. Each sugar has its own rate of crystallization; therefore, the presence of any other sugar(s) will delay or inhibit crystallization of sucrose.
    c. Fat and/or protein in a cooked, cooled sugar syrup may:
        (1) Foster formation of many, small crystals.
        (2) Delay or prevent crystallization of sucrose.
4. Syrups for amorphous candies are cooked to higher temperatures than syrups for crystalline candies.
5. Factors that prevent crystallization:
    a. An increased concentration of interfering agents inhibits and prevents crystallization.
    b. The higher the end temperature the greater the viscosity of the syrup.
    c. Stirring during cooking may be essential to prevent scorching of milk, chocolate or cocoa, or butter.
    d. Stirring must be kept at a minimum to prevent formation of nuclei.
    e. Cooked syrups must be cooked without agitation.

Note of caution: Temperatures used in sugar cookery—238–310°F (114–154°C)–are much above the boiling point of water. Handle hot syrups with *extreme caution!*

Comment: Traditionally "fondant" and "fudge" are crystalline candies. Sucrose is dissolved in water, the sugar solution is heated to a high temperature, 234–240°F (112–116°C), to produce a supersaturated sugar solution when the syrup is cooled. See principles, pages 231–232, for factors which affect the size of the sugar crystals during recrystallization. The smaller the crystals formed, the smoother and creamier the fondant or fudge.

Uncooked candies prepared from powdered sugar cannot be classified as true fondants or fudges because there is *no* control of the size of the sugar crystals.

Chocolate Fudge

Sugar, granulated	1 1/2 cups	375 ml
Milk	1/2 cup	125 ml
Corn syrup, light	2 tablespoons	30 ml
Chocolate	1 1/2 squares	1 1/2 squares
Butter or margarine	2 tablespoons	30 ml
Vanilla	1/2 teaspoon	2 ml
Nuts, coarsely broken (optional)	1/2 cup	125 ml

Butter or margarine to grease pie plate

1. Check boiling point of water on candy thermometer.
2. *Lightly* butter a 6-inch (15 cm) diameter glass pie plate.
3. Use a 5-cup (1.25 L) saucepan with a diameter of 6 inches (15 cm). Blend together the sugar, corn syrup, and milk. Stir with a wooden spoon. Place the candy thermometer in the saucepan.
4. Bring the mixture to 238°F (115°C) with as constant stirring as necessary to keep from scorching. Remember to adjust final temperature. If water boiled at 210°F (99°C), cook mixture to 236°F (114°C). During the cooking period it may be desirable to wipe undissolved sugar crystals from the side of the pan with a damp cheesecloth wrapped around a fork.
5. Remove pan from heat; add the butter and the chocolate. Do not cut up the chocolate before adding it to the cooked mixture. *Do not stir* the mixture, but allow the cooked syrup to cool to 110°F (43°C). If time is limited, it may be necessary to set the pan containing the cooked syrup into a pan of cold water to which 2 or 3 ice cubes have been added so the temperature can be reduced more quickly. It is *preferable* to reduce the heat without using the cold water.
6. Remove candy thermometer; add the vanilla; use a wooden spoon to beat mixture until the mass begins to hold its shape as the spoon is pulled through it. This beating may take as long as 20 minutes. Quickly add nuts (when used) and press the mixture into a buttered pie plate. *Do not* use nuts for class evaluation of crystalline candy.
7. Record total working time: _____ minutes.

Penuche Fudge

Light brown sugar	1 1/2 cups	375 ml
Half and Half (light cream)	1/2 cup	125 ml
Butter or margarine	2 tablespoons	30 ml
Vanilla	1/2 teaspoon	2 ml
Nuts, coarsely broken	1/2 cup	125 ml
Butter or margarine to grease pie plate		

1. Check boiling point of water on candy thermometer.
2. *Lightly* butter a 6-inch (15 cm) glass pie plate.
3. Use a 5-cup (1.25 L) saucepan 6 inches (15 cm) in diameter. Blend together the brown sugar and the Half and Half (light cream). Stir with a wooden spoon. Place the candy thermometer in the saucepan.
4. Bring the mixture to 238°F (115°C) with as constant stirring as necessary to keep mixture from scorching. Remember to adjust final temperature. If water boiled at 210°F (99°C), cook mixture to 236°F (114°C). During the cooking period it may be desirable to wipe undissolved sugar crystals from the side of the pan with a damp cheesecloth wrapped around a fork.
5. Remove pan from heat; add the butter. *Do not stir* the mixture, but allow the cooked syrup to cool to 110°F (43°C). If time is limited, it may be necessary to set the pan containing the cooked syrup into a pan of cold water to which 2 or 3 ice cubes have been added so the temperature can be reduced more quickly. It is *preferable* to reduce the heat without using the cold water bath.
6. Remove candy thermometer; add vanilla; use a wooden spoon to beat mixture until the mass begins to hold its shape as the spoon is pulled through it. This beating may take as long as 20 minutes. Quickly add nuts (when used) and press mixture into buttered pie plate. *Do not* use nuts for class evaluation of crystalline candy.
7. Record total working time:_____ minutes.

CHARACTERISTICS OF HIGH QUALITY CRYSTALLINE CANDIES

Appearance: Surface should have a high sheen; satiny.
Consistency: Firm enough to hold shape or cut edge when spooned into individual portions or when cut in pieces.
Texture: Smooth feel on tongue without stickiness (pastiness) or graininess; very fine crystals can be identified as portion of fudge is pressed against the roof of the mouth by the tongue.
Flavor: Sweetness well blended with other ingredients which may contribute to flavor as chocolate, vanilla, brown sugar. Nuts, when used, must be *fresh*.

Divinity Fudge

Sugar, granulated	1 cup	250 ml
Corn syrup, light	1/4 cup	50 ml
Water	1/4 cup	50 ml
Egg white	1	1
Vanilla	1/2 teaspoon	2 ml
Nut meats, broken	1/3 cup (optional)	75 ml

1. Check the temperature at which water boils vigorously on the candy thermometer.
2. Cover a baking sheet 12 X 14 inches (30 X 35 cm) with heavy waxed paper.
3. Use the upper section of the double boiler, 3-cup (750 ml) capacity, for a saucepan. (The narrow, deep pan holds the cooking syrup over the mercury bulb of the thermometer.)
4. Place the sugar, corn syrup, and water in the saucepan (see Step 3). Stir to blend ingredients; sugar will not be dissolved. Place candy thermometer in pan.
5. Place the pan over high heat to cook as rapidly as possible without having the syrup "boil over" the top of the pan. Cook to an end temperature of 264°F (130°C). If thermometer has shown water boils at 210°F (99°C) cook syrup to 262°F (128°C).
6. *Do not beat* egg white until syrup reaches 260°F (127°C). Place the egg white in a 1-1/2–2 quart (1.5–2 L) bowl; the bowl should be deep with a narrow bottom so the egg white will be easily caught into the egg beater. Use a hand electric mixer at highest speed to beat egg white until soft peaks form. The tips of the egg white fall over as the beater is removed. (Check page 124 for stages of beating egg white.)
7. Remove cooked syrup from the heat.
8. Pour the *hot* syrup in a *thin stream* (as thin as a thread) onto the beaten egg white with continuous beating. Have the mixer at highest speed. *Be sure the syrup goes onto the egg white and not into the beater blades nor into the sides of the bowl.* * Take 5 or more minutes to add the syrup to the egg white. *Do not scrape* the last portion of syrup from the pan.
9. Keep beating the mixture at highest speed until the mixture cools and begins to stiffen. Reduce mixer speed to medium and to low depending on the stiffness of the divinity mixture.
10. Stop the mixer and add the vanilla. Beat the divinity mixture at *lowest* mixer speed until the candy appears to hold its shape as the beater is pulled out of the candy. *This is a critical step.* The candy mixture must be beaten until crystallization begins; beating must be stopped before crystallization is completed.
11. If nuts are used, quickly add at this step. Do not have nuts cut too finely; this would detract from appearance. *Do not use* nuts for class evaluation.
12. Quickly drop candy onto waxed paper by teaspoons. Use one spoon to cut a portion of candy; use a second spoon to push the candy onto the waxed paper.
13. Record total working time: _____ minutes.

*Syrup hardens quickly and will gum up the beaters or form a heavy coating on the sides of the bowl.

CHARACTERISTICS OF HIGH QUALITY DIVINITY FUDGE (CRYSTALLINE CANDY)

Appearance: Slight sheen, white, opaque.
Texture: Very fine crystals, smooth.
Consistency: Firm enough to hold shape, yet soft to the bite.
Flavor: Sweet, mild vanilla when no nuts have been added.

Caramels

Sugar, granulated	1 cup	250 ml
Corn syrup, light	2/3 cup	150 ml
Sweetened condensed milk	2/3 cup	150 ml
Butter or margarine	1/2 cup	125 ml
Vanilla	1 teaspoon	5 ml
Brazil nuts, whole, unblanched	1 cup	250 ml

Butter or margarine to grease pan and knife to cut caramels

1. Check boiling point of water on candy thermometer.
2. Lightly butter the bottom and sides of a pan 7 × 7 inches (18 × 18 cm). When used, spread nuts evenly over the bottom of the pan.
3. Use a 5-cup (1.25 L) saucepan with a 6-inch (15 cm) diameter. Blend together the sugar, corn syrup, and butter. Bring to a boil with constant stirring.
4. Very gradually, with constant stirring, add the sweetened condensed milk. The milk should be added without reducing the boiling of the sugar syrup. Continue stirring the boiling mixture for 15 minutes. (Be sure to keep the bottom of the saucepan scraped clean. The sweetened condensed milk scorches very quickly; the scorched portions give lumpy caramels.)
5. Remove the saucepan from the heat and quickly and *carefully* put the candy thermometer in position. Return the caramel mixture to the heat. Cook with constant stirring to 246°F (119°C). Be sure to adjust final temperature; if water has boiled at 210°F (99°C) on the candy thermometer, remove cooked caramels at 244°F (118°C).
6. Remove from heat; remove candy thermometer; quickly stir in the vanilla. *Quickly* pour caramels into buttered pan. *Caution:* scrapings must be put into a second buttered pan.
7. When scraping the pan, remember the scrapings will be *very hot—do avoid burns*.
8. Allow caramels to set until cool. Then loosen caramels from sides of pan with case knife. Place heavy waxed paper on bread board. Invert caramels onto the waxed paper. If caramels have become cold, *lightly* warm the bottom of the pan to melt the fat so the caramels will fall free from the pan.
9. Cut individual caramels using a lightly buttered french knife and/or scissors. Wrap individual caramels in heavy waxed paper. Save for class evaluation.
10. Do not use nuts for class evaluation.
11. Record total working time: _____ minutes.

CHARACTERISTICS OF HIGH QUALITY CARAMEL CANDY

Appearance: Tan to brown color, medium brown being most desirable,* smooth with a sheen.

Texture and Tenderness: Firm, smooth feel in the mouth; acceptable texture may vary from being somewhat short (friable, easily broken) to being chewy without being gummy and sticky.

Flavor: Rich, sweet, a distinct flavor; well rounded.

*Color will be deep reddish brown if chocolate or cocoa is added.

Peanut Brittle

Sugar, granulated	1 1/2 cups	375 ml
Corn syrup, light	1/2 cup	125 ml
Water	1/2 cup	125 ml
Butter or margarine	3 tablespoons	45 ml
*Soda	1/2 teaspoon	2 ml
Peanuts, raw or roasted	1 1/2 cups	375 ml
Vanilla	1/2 teaspoon	2 ml

1. Check boiling point of water on candy thermometer.
2. Use 1 tablespoon (15 ml) of butter or margarine to lightly grease the surface of three inverted baking sheets, 10 1/2 X 15 1/2 inches (26 X 38 cm). (There should be no sides surrounding the surface used, as the sides interfere in the stretching or pulling of the cooked brittle.)
3. Use a saucepan of 2-quart (2 L) capacity with a diameter of 6 inches (15 cm). Combine the water, corn syrup, and sugar in the saucepan. Place the thermometer in position in the saucepan.
4. Heat the sugar mixture rapidly to 280°F (138°C). Stir as little as possible to keep mixture from scorching. It may be desirable to wipe undissolved sugar crystals from the side of the pan with damp cheesecloth wrapped around a fork.
5. When the syrup reaches 280°F (138°C), add the peanuts and the butter or margarine. Stir the mixture continuously and heat to 306°F (152°C). Remove pan from heat immediately. Remember to make temperature adjustments for original thermometer reading for boiling water; if water boiled at 210°F (99°C), cook to 304°F (151°C).
6. Add the soda and the vanilla; stir these ingredients in as quickly as possible. *Do not overstir* or the foam structure will be lost.
7. Pour approximately one third of the final mixture on each of the three baking sheets. Pour into as thin a layer as possible, but *do not* try to spread the mixture with a spatula.
8. After the edges of the candy have cooled slightly–about 2 minutes–start to gently pull and stretch the candy into a relatively thin sheet. Try to keep the nuts fairly evenly distributed during stretching. Continue to stretch the candy until the center of the mass has also been stretched.
9. Record total working time: _____ minutes.

*If soda is omitted, a very hard, glassy type peanut brittle will result.

CHARACTERISTICS OF HIGH QUALITY PEANUT BRITTLE

Appearance: Candy mass should appear somewhat aerated or foamy. The candy mass should be pale golden with the peanuts slightly darker.
Texture: Foam structure may not be apparent; candy mass is brittle and easily breaks up.
Flavor: Mild caramel flavor for the candy mass.

Lollipops or Hard Candy

Sugar, granulated	1 cup	250 ml
Corn syrup, light	1/3 cup	75 ml
Water	1/2 cup	125 ml

*Flavoring
*Coloring
Round toothpicks or wood skewers
Butter or margarine to grease baking sheets.

1. Check boiling point of water on candy thermometer.
2. Lightly grease the bottoms of two cookie sheets, 10 1/2 × 15 1/2 inches (26 × 38 cm). Use butter or margarine.
3. Cook sugar, corn syrup, and water to 310°F (154°C) with as little stirring as possible. It may be desirable to wipe undissolved sugar crystals from the side of the pan with a damp cheesecloth wrapped around a fork.
4. Remove the cooked syrup from the heat; quickly add the desired coloring and flavor ingredients *with as little stirring* as possible.
5. Use a metal tablespoon to quickly spoon the syrup onto the buttered baking pans. Try to keep the spooned mixture in rounds or "lollipop" shape. Round toothpicks or skewers can be quickly pressed onto the hot candies.
6. Carefully loosen the candies from the buttered baking sheet.
7. Record total working time: _____ minutes.

*If oils are used for flavoring—for example, oil of cloves—the quantity used for flavoring *can easily be less than one drop*. The amount of oil that can be held on the end of a toothpick may give an adequate amount of flavoring to the candy. Flavor extracts are less potent than oils as a source of flavor, but care should also be taken with extracts not to get too much extract in the candies. Coloring materials are also very concentrated so a *small* amount of coloring is added—again about as much as will remain on the end of a toothpick.

CHARACTERISTICS OF HIGH QUALITY HARD CANDIES

Appearance: Candies are generally translucent and solid without air bubbles.
Texture: Smooth with no graininess as the candy dissolves in the mouth.
Flavor: Distinct for type of flavoring used.

REVIEW QUESTIONS

1. Define or explain each of the following terms:
   a. Crystalline (candy).
   b. Amorphous (candy).
   c. Saturated solution.
   d. Supersaturation.
   e. Nuclei.
   f. Interfering (doctoring) agents.
   g. Hydrolysis.
   h. Sucrose.
   i. Invert sugar.
   j. Viscosity.
2. a. List the three essential steps in preparing any crystalline candy.
   b. Briefly describe each of the three steps.
   c. Indicate what is being accomplished at each step in regard to the crystalline structure of the candy.
3. a. Compare the ratio of sugar to corn syrup in the chocolate fudge recipe and the caramel recipe.
   b. Explain why the ratio differs for the two types of candy.
4. A recipe for chocolate fudge contains brown sugar, heavy cream, butter, and chocolate. What expectations might be held in regard to:
   a. Preparation?
   b. Finished product?
5. Discuss the importance of the degree of beating in making divinity (foam) fudge.
6. In making amorphous candies, what is the importance of each of the following steps?
   a. Stirring constantly to add milk.
   b. Not scraping the cooking pan after pouring candy.
   c. Cooking lollipops with minimal stirring.
7. Why is the baking soda used in making peanut brittle?

Crystallization: Water (Frozen Desserts)

OBJECTIVES

1. To acquaint the student with selected factors that affect crystallization of water to ice in frozen dessert mixtures.
   a. Chemical factors:
      (1) In the frozen dessert mixture:
         (a) Type and concentration of sugars.
         (b) Role of fat.
         (c) Non-fat milk solids.
         (d) Other solids.
         (e) Stabilizers and emulsifiers.
      (2) In the freezing mixture:
         (a) Ratio of ice to salt.
         (b) Role of water.
   b. Physical factors:
      (1) In the frozen dessert mixture.
         (a) Interfering substances.
         (b) Role of agitation.
         (c) Overrun.
         (d) Hardening.
      (2) In the frozen dessert mixture:
         (a) Role of agitation.
         (b) Rate of agitation.
2. To give students the opportunity to compare the texture and flavor of selected frozen desserts.

PRODUCTS TO BE PREPARED TO ILLUSTRATE PRINCIPLES

*Ice Creams:	*Sherbets:	Still Frozen:
Vanilla	Orange	Chocolate mousse
Chocolate		
Strawberry		

*Note: These products require not less than 3 hours preparation time. The ice cream mix can be prepared through Step 7 and held in the refrigerator. The freezing process (page 242) can then be started at the beginning of the laboratory period. The sherbet mix can be prepared through Step 4 and held in the freezer. At the start of the laboratory period, remove the frozen mix from the tray in chunks; hold at room temperature for about 5 minutes. Then proceed with Step 5.

PRINCIPLES

1. Frozen desserts consist of ice crystals suspended in a sugar syrup into which air bubbles have been beaten.
2. Sugars in solution:
   a. Lower the freezing point of the solution. One gram-molecular-weight of sugar lowers the freezing point by 1.86 degrees Celsius.
   b. In frozen dessert mixes act to control size of ice crystals.
3. Fats:
   a. Are interfering substances which cause more ice crystals to be formed.
   b. Affect the texture of the frozen desserts.
4. Milk:
   a. Solids affect the viscosity of the mix and aid in the incorporation of air into the mix.
   b. Sugar will affect the freezing point of the mix.
5. Gelatin and egg white may be added to a frozen dessert mix to increase viscosity and aid in the incorporation of air (overrun).
6. Emulsifiers are added to commercial ice cream mixes to aid in emulsification, viscosity, and foam stability.
7. Agitation (rapid mixing) when the mix is close to the freezing point favors the formation of many small crystals.
8. Frozen desserts need to be hardened after the freezing process has been terminated. The hardness of the frozen dessert will depend upon:
   a. The lowest temperature reached.
   b. Quantity of sugar in the mix.

PRINCIPLES: Freezing Desserts in an Ice Cream Freezer

1. The freezer is designed so the mix will be well agitated during the freezing process.
2. The freezing mixture consists of ice, salt, and brine.
3. Salt is more effective than sugar in lowering the freezing point.
4. The brine absorbs the heat from the frozen dessert mix.

Vanilla Ice Cream—Custard Base

Note: This is a variation of the method presented in the Starch-Egg Chapter (page 135).

Milk	2 cups	500 ml
Sugar	3/4 cup	175 ml
Half and Half	1 cup	250 ml
Heavy cream	1 cup	250 ml
Eggs (beaten)	2	2
Flour	1 tablespoon	15 ml
Salt	1/4 teaspoon	1 ml
Vanilla	2 teaspoons	10 ml

1. Combine milk, flour, and salt in a 2 quart (2 L) saucepan. Heat on medium, with constant stirring, to boiling; boil for 1 minute.
2. Cool pan until you can hold your hand on the bottom of the pan.
3. Add sugar and beaten egg by adding 2 tablespoons of the warm mixture to the mixed sugar and egg. Then add this mixture back to the pan containing the milk and flour.
4. Return the pan to the heat and stir constantly until slightly thickened.
5. Cool by placing pan in sink in cold water.
6. Add Half and Half, cream, and vanilla; mix well.
7. Chill the mixture well then freeze according to directions.

VARIATIONS

Chocolate Ice Cream
Add 2 ounces of unsweetened chocolate to cold milk and allow to melt as milk mixture is heated. Beat with a rotary beater until smooth.

Strawberry or Raspberry Ice Cream
When ready to freeze, stir in one pint of crushed sweetened berries; *omit* the vanilla.

FREEZING

1. Use finely crushed ice and rock salt.
2. Mix ice (5 parts) and salt (1 part) in a plastic dish pan.
3. Place beaters in the can and put can in the tub. Be sure that the socket hole in the bottom of the can rests on the center point of the casting in the bottom of the tub.
4. Pour in mixture—never over 3/4 full.
5. Adjust cover and gear frame—fasten down latch(es).
6. Pack ice/salt mixture around the can covering it completely.
7. Turn occasionally while packing. Allow to stand 1 minute after packing.
8. Turn on motor and beat until hard to turn.
9. Remove the beaters and scrape the ice cream into the can. Be careful not to let any salt/ice/brine mixture get into the can. Replace cover and plug hole tightly.
10. Allow the ice cream to ripen (harden) for 30–60 minutes.
11. Record total working time:_____ minutes

CHARACTERISTICS OF HIGH QUALITY ICE CREAM

Appearance: Color according to flavor
Vanilla, creamy white to light yellow.
Chocolate, medium chocolate brown (slight red cast if "Dutched" cocoa is used).
Strawberry, creamy pink; strawberry seeds may show.
Raspberry, bluish pink; pieces of fruit may show.
Consistency: Firm enough to hold shape.
Texture: Should feel smooth (fine crystals) on the tongue.
Body: Thick and smooth as it begins to melt.
Flavor: Slightly sweet characteristic of flavor.

Chocolate Mousse

Chocolate chips, semi-sweet	1 cup	250 ml
Water, boiling	1/2 cup	125 ml
Eggs, separated	4	4
Vanilla	2 teaspoons	10 ml
Sugar	1 tablespoon	15 ml
Cream, heavy	1 cup	250 ml
Almonds, toasted and slivered	2 tablespoons	30 ml

1. Put the chocolate chips and boiling water into a blender; mix at "Blend" (3/4 maximum speed) for 1 minute. Cool.
2. Add egg yolks and vanilla; mix at "Blend" for 1 minute.
3. Beat egg whites in a large mixing bowl, adding sugar gradually, to the stiff peak stage.
4. Fold chocolate mixture into beaten egg whites.
5. Whip the heavy cream to stiff peak stage and fold into the chocolate-egg white mixture.
6. Pour into serving dishes and freeze to soft stage.
7. Record total working time: _____ minutes.

CHARACTERISTICS OF HIGH QUALITY CHOCOLATE MOUSSE

Appearance: Medium chocolate brown; may have slight red cast.
Consistency: Firm enough to hold shape.
Texture: Should feel smooth (fine crystals) on the tongue.
Body: Medium thick and smooth as it begins to melt.
Flavor: Sweet; distinct chocolate flavor.

Orange Sherbet

Milk, whole	2 cups	500 ml
Gelatin, plain	1 envelope (1/4 oz)	7 gm
Sugar	1 cup	250 ml
Orange juice	1 cup	250 ml
Lemon juice, fresh	2 tablespoons	30 ml
Salt	1/2 teaspoon	2 ml
Yellow food color	6 drops	6 drops
Red food color	3 drops	3 drops

1. Place only 1 cup of milk in a 2 quart (2 L) saucepan; sprinkle gelatin over the surface; allow to stand for 5 minutes.
2. Heat slowly with constant stirring gelatin "dissolves".
3. Remove from heat and add all of the other ingredients; stir until the sugar is dissolved.
4. Pour into a 9" X 9" (23 cm X 23 cm) aluminum pan; cover pan with plastic wrap or foil and place in the freezer. Freeze until firm and hard (1 1/2–2 hours).
5. Remove from freezer; cut into chunks and put into a large bowl (3–4 quarts); allow to stand for 10 minutes to soften.
6. Beat until it increases in volume and becomes smooth (do not allow to melt); pour back into the pan; recover and return to the freezer.
7. Allow to freeze until just firm (about 1 hour). Remove and serve.
8. Record total working time: _____ minutes.

Alternate freezing method

Mix: follow steps 1, 2, and 3 above.
Freeze in ice cream freezer—see directions for vanilla ice cream on page 242.

CHARACTERISTICS OF HIGH QUALITY SHERBET

Appearance: Color according to flavor; should be a muted shade.
Consistency: Firm enough to hold shape.
Texture: Should feel smooth (fine crystals) on the tongue.
Body: Thin to medium thick and smooth as it begins to melt.
Flavor: Sweet note but also a tart note; characteristic orange flavor.

EVALUATION OF PRODUCTS
(Frozen Dessert)

Name: _____

Date: _____

Score System

Points	Quality
7	Excellent
6	Very good
5	Good
4	Medium
3	Fair
2	Poor
1	Very poor

Directions:

1. Place the numerical score in the box in the upper left hand corner.
2. Comments should justify the numerical score. Comments must be brief.
3. Evaluation of the food products must be on an *individual* basis.

Products

Quality Characteristic					
Appearance					
Consistency					
Texture					
Body					
Flavor					

REVIEW QUESTIONS

1. Define or explain each of the following terms:
   a. Heat of Fusion.
   b. Molal Lowering of Freezing Point.
   c. Viscosity.
   d. Crystallization.
   e. Brine.
2. Explain the role of each of the following ingredients or procedures in ice crystal formation:
   a. Sugar (2 ways).
   b. Fat.
   c. Non-fat milk solids.
   d. Other solids (eggs, gelatin).
   e. Emulsifiers.
   f. Agitation.
3. Discuss the ratio of salt to ice in the freezing mixtures for ice cream as contrasted with sherbet.
4. Why is it necessary to be careful to keep the salt/ice/brine mixture from getting into the frozen dessert?
5. a. When ice cream is held in storage, how can the growth of ice crystals be inhibited?
   b. How would growth of ice crystals affect the quality of any frozen dessert?

Microwave Cooking

OBJECTIVES

1. To introduce and apply the basic principles of microwave cooking.
2. To illustrate principles using various techniques of microwave cooking with selected foods.

PRODUCTS TO BE PREPARED TO ILLUSTRATE PRINCIPLES

Cinnamon sugar muffins
Chocolate pudding
*Cheese sauce
*Baked custard
Scrambled eggs
*Floating island
Bacon

Ground beef patty
Vegetables
  Broccoli
  Baked potatoes
  Savory spinach
Applesauce
White sauce

*Require a microwave oven with variable power capability.

PRINCIPLES

1. Microwaves have very short wave lengths; less than five inches for microwaves used to heat foods.
2. Microwaves may behave in three ways:
   a. Be absorbed by the material causing heating; this causes the cooking of food.
   b. Pass through the material with no reaction; substances exhibiting this property may be used as containers for the food in microwave ovens.
   c. Bounce off metals thereby limiting the use of metals in microwave cooking.
3. Microwaves penetrate the food from all directions.
4. Microwaves reverse direction 2,450,000,000 times a second causing the food molecules to vibrate. The friction of the molecules in motion generates heat, which cooks the food very quickly.
5. Microwaves penetrate food to a depth of 3/4–1 1/2 inches causing heating in the area which they penetrate. Heat is transferred to the center (cold area) by conduction which is the mechanism of heat transfer in conventional cooking.
6. Some foods may cook further after removal from the oven.
7. The rate of cooking is influences by many factors:
   a. Water, fat, and sugar absorb microwave energy more readily and therefore cook faster.
   b. Well marbled meat cooks more evenly.

    c. Small amounts of food cook faster than large amounts.

    d. Thinner parts of foods which are not evenly shaped cook faster than thicker parts.

    e. Porous foods absorb energy more reasily and cook faster than denser foods.

    f. Bone conducts heat and may cause uneven heating if it is on one side of a cut of meat. Boneless cuts of meat cook more slowly but more evenly.

8. Covering the food container will speed up cooking. Microwave cooking is essentially a moist heat method of cooking.

9. Some food products brown in the microwave oven while others do not. Large items (such as a whole turkey) which have a long cooking time (60–90 minutes) will brown. Small items (such as cup cakes) which have a short cooking time (2–4 minutes) do not brown; moisture on the surface of the cup cake would also be a factor in preventing browning.

10. It may be necessary to stir the food, to rearrange it in the pan or to rotate the pan to get more even heating.

SPECIAL NOTE

The cooking times given in these recipes are based on a microwave oven with an output of 600–700 watts. If the oven used does not have an output within this range, adjustments in cooking time will be required; for ovens with an output of less than 600 watts, a longer cooking time will be required while ovens with an output of more than 700 watts will require a shorter cooking time. The total power consumption of a microwave oven will always be greater than the actual cooking power (output). The total power consumption will be about 1500 watts.

The products prepared in the microwave oven should be evaluated using the appropriate "Characteristics of High Quality Products." Cross references will be given after each recipe in this section.

Cinnamon Sugar Muffins

Flour, all-purpose	1 cup	250	ml
Baking powder	2 teaspoons	10	ml
Salt	1/2 teaspoon	2	ml
Sugar	3 tablespoons	45	ml
Milk	1/2 cup	125	ml
Egg, blended	2 tablespoons	30	ml
Vegetable oil	2 tablespoons	30	ml

Topping

Sugar	2 tablespoons	30	ml
Cinnamon	1/8 teaspoon	0.5	ml

1. Sift together flour, baking powder, salt and 3 tablespoons (30 ml) sugar.
2. Use a rotary egg beater to thoroughly blend milk, egg, and vegetable oil so the oil is in fine globules when liquid ingredients are added to dry ingredients.
3. Add liquid to dry ingredients. Stir 15–20 strokes; all dry ingredients should be wetted, but the batter should still be lumpy.
*4. Carefully spoon batter into custard cups; do not fill more than half-full.
5. Spoon some of the topping over each muffin.
6. Do not microwave more than 6 muffins at one time. Place custard cups in a circle in the oven. Microwave at *high* power for 1 minute; turn 1/2 turn. Microwave 1 more minute at *high* power; turn 1/4 turn. Microwave 30 seconds at *high* power or until muffins appear to be baked. Tops may be slightly moist but will dry with standing. *Avoid overbaking.*
7. Remove muffins immediately from custard cups; place muffins on cooling rack.
8. Record total working time: _____ minutes.
9. Refer to page 22 for characteristics for high quality muffins.

*Only custard cups made of materials safe for microwave cooking may be used. Bottoms of glass custard cups can be greased and batter put directly into the custard cups or cup-cake paper cups can be used in the custard cups; two paper liners are used in each cup. Paper liners are to be filled no more than half-full.

White Sauce

Flour, all-purpose	2 tablespoons	30 ml
Butter or margarine	2 tablespoons	30 ml
Salt	1/4 teaspoon	1 ml
Milk	1 cup	250 ml

1. Put butter or margarine into a 1-quart (1 L) glass measuring cup. Microwave at *high* power for 30 seconds or until fat has melted.
2. Add flour and salt; stir until thoroughly blended; add milk gradually and stir continuously to evenly disperse the flour.
3. Microwave at *high* power for 30 seconds; stir thoroughly to prevent starch from settling to the bottom of container. Microwave for 30 seconds at *high* power; stir thoroughly; microwave for 30 seconds; stir thoroughly. If the sauce has not boiled, heat an additional 30 seconds or more until the sauce does boil. If the sauce has been cooked sufficiently, it will have the consistency of a medium white sauce.
4. Record total working time: _____ minutes.
5. Refer to page 92 for characteristics for high quality white sauce.

Cheese Sauce

Cheddar cheese, grated	1/2 cup	125 ml

Medium white sauce as prepared on page 250

1. After the white sauce has boiled as indicated in Step 3, allow the sauce to cool for 2 or 3 minutes. Add the grated cheese. Blend cheese thoroughly.
2. If the cheese does not melt completely, microwave at *medium* power (50%) for 10 seconds; stir. If more heat is necessary, continue heating for *short* intervals.
3. Record total working time:_____ minutes.
4. Refer to page 181 for characteristics of high quality cheese sauce.

Chocolate Pudding

		1/2 square
Chocolate	1/2 square	15 ml
Water	1 tablespoon	250 ml
Milk	1 cup	45 ml
Cornstarch	1 tablespoon +	
	1 teaspoon	20 ml
Sugar	3 tablespoons	45 ml
Salt	few grains	few grains
Vanilla	1/4 teaspoon	1 ml

1. In a 1-cup (250 ml) glass measure, put water and chocolate broken into several pieces. Microwave at *high* for 30 seconds. Thoroughly stir until a smooth paste forms. Add approximately 1/4 of the milk. Stir until evenly blended. There should not be lumps of chocolate at this stage.
2. In a 1-quart (1 L) glass measure, combine the cornstarch, sugar, salt and remaining milk. Stir until evenly blended; there should not be lumps of unblended cornstarch at this stage.
3. Add the chocolate-milk mixture to the starch mixture. Stir until thoroughly blended. Microwave at *high* for 30 seconds; stir.
4. Microwave for 30 seconds at *high* power 4 more times (for 2 minutes); stir after each 30 second heating period. If the pudding has boiled up in the cup during the last 30 second heating period and the pudding appears to be thick, no further cooking is necessary. If the pudding has not boiled or does not appear thick, microwave at *high* power until the pudding does boil. If more cooking is necessary, heat the pudding for 15 seconds for these final stages of heating.
5. Add vanilla to the cooked pudding. Stir until blended. Pour pudding into 2 serving dishes.
6. Record total working time: _____ minutes.
7. Refer to page 92 for characteristics for a high quality chocolate pudding.

Scrambled Eggs

Eggs	2	2	
Milk	2 tablespoons	30	ml
Salt	1/8 teaspoon	0.5	ml
Butter or margarine	1 teaspoon	5	

1. Place butter or margarine into a 2 cup (500 ml) microwave cooking container. Microwave at *high* for 15 seconds or until fat is melted.
2. In a small size bowl combine eggs, milk and salt. Beat until egg yolks and whites are thoroughly blended, but not foamy. Pout into melted fat.
3. Microwave at *high* for 30 seconds; stir. Microwave for another 30 seconds at *high* power; stir.
4. Microwave for another 30 seconds at *high*; at this point the eggs will appear moist and slightly creamy; they are servable as the eggs will continue to cook for a short time. However, the eggs can be cooked to a greater degree of doneness by heating at 5 second intervals. Care must be used to avoid overcooking.
5. Record total working time: _____ minutes.
6. Refer to page 000 for characteristics for high quality scrambled eggs.

Baked Custard

Milk	2 cups	500	ml
Eggs	3	3	
Sugar	1/4 cup	50	ml
Salt	1/8 teaspoon	0.5	ml
Vanilla	1/2 teaspoon	2	
Nutmeg			

1. With a rotary beater blend together all ingredients except the nutmeg. The egg whites should be thoroughly blended but NOT foamy. Strain mixture into 4 small size custard cups. Sprinkle a few grains of nutmeg on each.
2. Baking time is dependent on number of custards baked at one time as well as temperature of ingredients at time of mixing and proportion of ingredients. Suggested cooking time at *low* power (20%): microwave 3 minutes; turn baking pan 1/4 turn and turn each custard cup 1/4 turn; microwave 3 minutes; turn baking pan 1/4 turn and turn each custard cup an additional 1/4 turn; microwave 3 minutes; turn baking pan 1/4 turn and turn custard cups an additional 1/4 turn. Check degree of coagulation by inserting the tip of a paring knife into the custard that seems to have the greatest degree of coagulation. The paring knife should come out "clean" if the custard is baked sufficiently. If further heating is necessary, microwave at *low* power (20%) for intervals of 30 seconds or for 1 minute intervals depending on the degree of coagulation observed when testing. Do not allow custards to "boil" as they are being baked. Some heating continues after the custards are removed from the oven. Each custard should be removed as it appears to be sufficiently coagulated.
3. Record total working time: _____ minutes.
4. Refer to page 000 for characteristics of high quality baked custards.

Floating Island — Stirred Custard Dessert

Meringues

Egg whites, room temperature	2	2
Sugar, finely granulated	1/4 cup	50 ml
Vanilla	1/4 teaspoon	1 ml

1. Place egg whites into a 1-quart (1 L) or small bowl. Add vanilla. Beat with rotary beater until the whites will form soft peaks as the beater is pulled from the foam.
2. Add the sugar gradually, beating only enough after each addition to blend sugar with foam. At the end of the beating period the egg whites should form fairly stiff peaks which slightly bend over at the tips. The sugar should be practically dissolved; the foam should not appear grainy.
3. Cut a piece of heavy, brown paper to fit a baking sheet.
4. Use 2 teaspoons to form 18–20 "islands"; place "islands" on brown paper.
5. Slide the brown paper off the baking sheet so it is on the floor of the oven. Microwave at *medium* (50%) power for 1 minute; turn 1/4 turn; microwave for 1 minute at *medium* (50%); turn 1/4 turn; microwave 1 minute at *medium* (50%) power. "Islands" should be firm to touch although the surface may be slightly moist. Slide paper back onto baking sheet to remove "islands" from the oven. Transfer the "islands" onto the cooked, stirred custard. (Recipe follows).
6. Refer to page 130 for characteristics of high quality meringues.

Custard

Milk	1 1/2 cups	375 ml
Egg yolks (from eggs used in meringues)	2	2
Egg, whole	1	1
Sugar	1/4 cup	50 ml
Vanilla	1/2 teaspoon	2 ml

1. Use a rotary beater to blend together the milk, sugar, egg yolks and egg. This mixture should be beaten until the egg white is blended; mixture should not be beaten until it is foamy. Strain into a 1-quart (1 L) glass measure.
2. Microwave at *high* power for approximately 6 minutes or until the custard coats the spoon. Size and shape of cooking utensil affect total cooking time, as does temperature of mix at beginning of cooking period. Suggested cooking times: at *high* power: 2 minutes; stir thoroughly; 1 minute; stir thoroughly, 1 minute, stir; 15 seconds, stir; 15 seconds, stir; 15 seconds, stir; 15 seconds, stir. As the temperature of the custard mix rises, stirring becomes very important. Cook at 5, 10, or 15 second intervals to bring the custard to the stage at which it will coat a metal spoon.
3. Pour cooked custard into a cold serving dish immediately after removing it from the microwave oven. Add the vanilla; stir to thoroughly blend. Place the cooked meringues on the top of the custard. Cool and serve.
4. Record total working time: _____ minutes.
5. Refer to page 119 for characteristics of high quality stirred custard.

Ground Beef Patty

Ground beef	4 ounces	125 ml
Liquid margarine	1 teaspoon	5 ml

1. Preheat browning grill for 8 minutes at *high* power in the microwave oven. Do NOT heat longer than 8 minutes.
*2. While grill is heating, shape meat into a patty 3/8–1/2 inch (1 cm–1.3 cm) thick. Add about half the fat to the surface of patty being browned.
3. Place patty on heated grill. Turn patty when it appears well-browned (about 2 minutes). Brown patty on second side. Time for browning is dependent on temperature of meat as well as number of patties being cooked at one time.
4. Microwave at *high* power to complete cooking, approximately 30 seconds for 1 patty.
5. Record total working time: _____ minutes.
6. Refer to page 142 for characteristics of high quality cooked meat.**

*If no browning grill is available, microwave at high power for 1-1/2 minutes on each side for 1 patty.
**Patty not cooked on heated browning grill will have characteristics of steamed meat.

Bacon

Bacon, sliced	1 or 2 slices

1. If bacon fat is to be used at a later time, place bacon slices on a trivet or on the bottom of a microwave dish.
2. If bacon fat is not to be saved, place bacon strips on a double layer of paper toweling placed on a ceramic plate suitable for microwave cooking.
3. In either Step 1 or Step 2 lay a piece of paper toweling on top of the bacon to avoid spattering as the bacon cooks.
4. Microwave at *high* power for 3/4–1 minute for each slice of bacon.
5. Total cooking time: _____ minutes.
6. Refer to page 139 for characteristics of high quality bacon.

Applesauce

Apples, cooking, medium size	3	3
Water	2 teaspoons	10 ml
Sugar	2–3 tablespoons	30–45 ml
No spice for class		

1. Wash apples; peel using a vegetable peeler. Quarter each apple; remove core; cut each quarter in half lengthwise.
2. Place prepared fruit in a 1-quart (1 L) casserole. Add water. Cover casserole with a piece of waxed paper.
3. Microwave at *high* power for 2 minutes; stir. Microwave at *high* for 1 more minute.
4. Add sugar; amount of sugar will vary with the variety of apple used and the degree of ripeness of the apples. Stir in the sugar. If the fruit slices are not yet tender enough to be broken up by stirring, microwave at *high* power for 30 second intervals. Amount of heat will depend on amount of fruit being cooked as well as on the variety and degree of ripeness of the apples.
5. Record total working time: _____ minutes.
6. Refer to page 189 for characteristics of high quality applesauce.

Baked Potatoes

Baking potatoes, medium   3

1. Thoroughly wash potatoes; use vegetable brush to scrub dirt from skin. Rinse and dry.
2. Prick through skin of potatoes 4 or 5 times on each side. Use a fork.
3. Arrange potatoes in a circular pattern on a microwave tray or on a piece of paper toweling.
4. Microwave at *high* power for 3 minutes; rearrange potatoes on tray and turn them over so the side that had been on top becomes the underside. Microwave at *high* power for 3 minutes; rearrange potatoes on tray. Microwave at *high* power for 3 minutes; check for degree of tenderness; potatoes will cook for a short time after being removed from oven. Continue microwaving at *high* power as needed for 30 second or 1 minute intervals.
5. Record total working time: _____ minutes.
6. Refer to page 172 for characteristics of high quality baked potatoes.

Savory Spinach

Leaf spinach, frozen	1 package	1 package
Bacon slices	4	4
Onion, medium	1	1
Sweet pickle relish	2 tablespoons	30 ml

1. Cut each bacon slice into 6–8 pieces; place pieces in a 2-quart microwave casserole; cover with wax paper. Microwave at *high* power 2–3 minutes or until bacon is crisp. Remove bacon pieces from fat.
2. Remove dry skin from onion; wash, dry and cut into coarse dice. Add onion to bacon fat; cover casserole with waxed paper. Microwave at *high* power until onion is translucent, 2–3 minutes.
3. Defrost spinach: follow package directions or defrost at *medium* power for 3–5 minutes. Place frozen spinach directly on top of cooked onions in casserole dish; if dish will not tolerate freezing as well as boiling temperatures, defrost the spinach in a separate container.
4. Add the defrosted spinach to the casserole containing the cooked onions. Cut through the spinach 6–8 times with a scissors to facilitate serving. Cover casserole; microwave at *high* power for 5 minutes or until the stems of the spinach are tender.
5. Add pickle relish. Microwave at *high* power for 15–20 seconds to heat relish.
6. Top with crisp bacon pieces for serving.
7. Total cooking time:_____minutes.
8. Refer to page 181 for characteristics of high quality cooked vegetables.

Broccoli

Fresh	1 pound	450 g
or		
Frozen	10 ounce package	283 g package

Fresh Broccoli

1. Wash and trim broccoli. If stem ends are tough, remove outer woody portion. Center portion of stems is edible.
2. Cut broccoli pieces so bud portions are approximately 4 inches (10 cm) long. Less tender stem portions can be cooked for a few minutes before bud ends are added to cooking dish.
3. If stem ends are to be cooked first, place them evenly in a baking dish. Add 1-2 tablespoons (15-30 ml) of water. Cover baking dish with waxed paper.
4. Microwave at *high* power for 3 minutes; turn baking dish 1/4 turn and rearrange broccoli stems so thicker portions remain to the outside of the dish. Cover and microwave for an additional 3 minutes at *high* power.
5. Place bud portion of broccoli in baking dish so buds are toward the center with the heavier stem portions toward the outside of the cooking dish. Cover with waxed paper; microwave at *high* power for 5 minutes; turn baking dish 1/4 turn; microwave 5 minutes. Test stem portion to check degree of doneness. If further cooking is required, microwave at *high* power for 3 minutes. Be careful; avoid overcooking.
6. Broccoli may be served with cheese sauce (see separate recipe page 251) or 1 teaspoon of butter or margarine may be melted for each serving of broccoli and spooned over the vegetable.
7. Record total working time: _____ minutes.
8. Refer to page 181 for characteristics of high quality cooked vegetable.

Frozen Broccoli

1. Remove packaging wrap from broccoli; place the frozen vegetable in a 1-2 quart (1-2 L) casserole dish. Cover dish with waxed paper.
2. Microwave at *medium* power (50%) for 2 minutes; separate stalks of broccoli as they become defrosted. Remove defrosted stalks and microwave remaining stalks at *medium* power for 30 seconds.
3. When all stalks have been defrosted, arrange the stalks in the casserole so the bud ends are to the center of the casserole and the stem ends are to the outside of the casserole. Cover the casserole with waxed paper.
4. Microwave at *high* power for 3 minutes; turn casserole 1/4 turn; microwave for 3 minutes. Check a stem portion for degree of tenderness. Microwave for 2 or 3 minute intervals at *high* power to reach the desired degree of tenderness. Avoid overcooking.
5. Follow Steps (6), (7), and (8) above to complete product and assignment.

REVIEW QUESTIONS

1. Explain how microwaves cause heating in foods.
2. Why can paper, some glass and some plastics be used as containers to hold food while it is being cooked in a microwave oven?
3. a. Explain why scrambled eggs can not be cooked in a stainless steel bowl.
   b. What else would happen if metal pans were used in a microwave oven?
4. Relate cooking time to quantity of food being cooked.
5. Discuss the effect of shape in cooking:
   a. A chicken leg and thigh.
   b. Fresh broccoli spears.
6. Fat comes to the surface of a whole turkey being cooked in the microwave oven. What effect will this have on browning? On juiciness?

Appliances for Food Preparation

OBJECTIVES

1. To list and discuss briefly small appliances for use in food preparation.
2. To present recipes and methods utilizing selected appliances suitable for use in a 2 hour laboratory period.

PRODUCTS TO BE DISCUSSED

Alternative or Supplemental to Range/Oven

Microwave oven
Electric fry pan
Slow cooker
Pressure cooker
Broiler–Rotisserie–Toaster oven
Cooker–Fryer
Casserole
Griddle
Convection oven
Roaster–oven

Specialized Purpose Appliances

Waffle baker–Sandwich grill
Toaster
Coffee maker, Automatic Drip
Ice cream freezer
Chafing dish/Fondue pot
WOK

Time Savers

Pressure cooker
Slicing knife
Microwave oven
Mixer
Blender
Food processor

INTRODUCTION

In recent years a large number of portable appliances have become available for use in the home; most of these appliances are electric and can be classified in three catagories:

1. Alternative or Supplemental to Range/Oven
2. Specialized Purpose
3. Time Savers

Some appliances, of course, may fall into more than one classification.

With careful selection, planning, and management, the small appliances could replace the range and oven in a very small kitchen. For certain types of cooking, a small appliance could be used instead of the range; for example, a crock pot could be used to make chili with a substantial saving in energy. For a large family dinner, small appliances may be used to provide extra cooking capacity; the microwave oven serves admirably for this purpose.

Most of the small appliances have a power rating of 1300–1500 watts which is about the same power rating as the small surface unit on an electric range operating at one-half power. Using them will result in energy savings. Further, there is a saving in power because it takes less energy to heat a toaster oven than a full size oven. Practically all small appliances have a thermostat so that there will be times when the power will be off, giving further energy savings. A regular oven is rated at 3200 watts while the broiler unit is rated at 3600 watts; a convection oven and a broiler-rotisserie each have a rating of 1500 watts and are thermostatically controlled.

A food processor may give a novice cook skills in cutting and slicing not possible with a knife; this would also offer some saving in time. The microwave oven is a great time (and energy) saver; a 12-pound turkey can be cooked in 1 1/2–2 1/2 hours rather than 4 hours in a full size oven. It is much quicker and easier to slice the turkey with an electric slicing knife. Other examples of time saving could be given.

Teflon® Coating

Most of the small appliances discussed here will have a Teflon® coating on the surface which comes in contact with the food to prevent sticking and in some instances, may offer other advantages. When using Teflon® coated appliances, plastic spatulas or turners are desirable to avoid scratching the coating but regular utensils may be used, carefully. Do *not* use metal scouring pads or steel wool to clean a Teflon® coated pan.

Watts in parentheses following the name of an appliance, as "Microwave Oven (1500 watts)," refers to the power or energy rating of the appliance.

APPLIANCES ALTERNATIVE OR SUPPLEMENTAL TO RANGE/OVEN

Microwave Oven (1500 watts)
Refer to chapter on Microwave Cooking pages 248–257

Electric Fry Pan (1000–1500 watts)
The most popular size is 11 inch or 12 inch square pan (provides more cooking surface); most are Teflon® coated. Covers range from 2 inches to 5 inches in depth but dome covers are also available; most covers have steam vents. These pans can be used for pan broiling or frying (page 138) and for braising (page 147–150) or in other applications where it is necessary to retain moisture and/or heat during serving as in one dish meals (pages 101–102), Hamburger Skillet Meal (page 101), and Hot Potato Salad (page 206).

When using an electric fry pan that is Teflon® coated, *less* fat is required when pan frying than when using a non-coated pan. The food will cook with *no added* fat but will not brown as well as it does with a small amount (1/4–1/3 usual amount) of fat in the recipe.

Slow Cookers (75–150 watts)
Because of the low power rating, food can be cooked for long periods of time without sticking or burning. However, the low wattage will not permit the meat to brown. Meat cooked in a slow cooker is cooked by moist heat.

Slow cookers appear to be of two basic types: (1) crockery which can not be placed over direct heat and (2) metal base with a heat proof glass top; this base can be placed over direct heat to brown meat before the cooker is placed on its heating element. If browned meat is desired in using the crockery cooker, the meat must be browned in a separate pan and then transferred to the crockery cooker.

Pressure Saucepan (1300 watts)
This is a moist heat method of cooking where the temperature will be increased to 240–250°F (115–121°C) by cooking in a sealed container which can be brought to internal pressure of 10–15 psi (pounds per square inch). At the higher cooking temperatures, cooking time is substantially reduced. Chicken Thighs (page 146), Spiced Veal Tongue (page 148) and Lamb Stew (page 151) are cooked in the pressure saucepan.

Broilers, Including Grill, Toaster, Rotisserie and/or Oven (1320–1650 watts)
The primary advantage of these appliances is that the entire large oven does not need to be heated and cleaned and the portability of the appliance. Meat can be broiled or roasted, and with a rotisserie, an entire fowl or roast of meat may be successfully prepared. The appliance may be used as a small oven and other food may be toasted or baked (see pages 138–139 for broiling and roasting meat and pages 159–162 for fish recipes).

Cooker–Fryer (1350–1500 watts)
This appliance may still be used as a deep fat fryer or it can be used for braising or stewing; it can be used to heat rolls and buns and to keep foods hot for a buffet (see page 141 and 147–150 for meat recipes; pages 83–88 for deep fat frying; pages 177–181 and 183–185 for vegetables).

Casseroles (1350 watts)

These appliances vary in size and the user must determine the appropriate one. They are not suitable for frying meat, deep fat frying, or baking. Electric casseroles are fully automatic and are capable of holding cooked food at serving temperature. The legume recipes (pages 183–185 and some of the vegetable recipes (pages 171–181) could be cooked in a casserole.

Griddles or Grills (1300–1500 watts)

Griddles are of variable size and have continuous control of temperature from "warm" to 450°F. Many of the portable griddles are constructed so that any fat which cooks out of the food can be collected in a container or cup. Griddles are most useful for pan-broiling (see pages 138 and 120) and can be used for frying eggs or pancakes, toasting English muffins, grilling sandwiches or cooking fruit or vegetables. A griddle can also be used as a hot tray for keeping food warm for serving.

Convection Oven (1500 watts)

A convection oven can be used for the same purposes as a regular oven; however, the cavity in a convection oven is smaller than the cavity in a regular oven and can not accommodate large roast or turkeys. This type of oven has a fan to circulate the heated air; thus food can be roasted or baked at lower temperatures and/or for shorter times.

Roaster Ovens (1300–1500 watts)

The large roasters are of 18-quart capacity and can hold a 20-pound turkey. Pies and cakes can be baked in this appliance or a full meal for a family or six may be cooked at one time. It may also be used to blanch vegetables for freezing. The capacity makes it useful for cooking large quantities of soup, stews, spaghetti, or other foods for entertaining. The temperature is automatically regulated between 200–500°F (93–260°C).

SUMMARY

Most of these appliances are energy efficient and perform many different types of cooking. There is also some duplication of uses of these appliances.

SPECIALIZED PURPOSE APPLIANCES

Waffle Baker/Sandwich Grills (825–1400 watts)

These appliances are rectangular (10" X 12") or square (9" X 9") both making 4 section waffles; alternate plates are for use as a grill. Both types of plates are available with Teflon® coating. The adjustable thermostat provides a temperature of 225–475°F (107–246°C).

When used as a grill, the appliance can be opened flat to grill bacon and other small cuts of meat, eggs, French toast, sliced fruits, and vegetables. When closed, both sides of the food are cooked at the same time. It will grill sandwiches, ham slices, cube steaks, and other small cuts of meat that can be cooked by dry heat and do not lose much fat during cooking.

Toasters (2 slice, 750-1100 watts; 4 slice, 1450-1650 watts)

There are now two types of toasters, wall type and oven type; the former is the most common. The wall type is available in 2 and 4 slice models. The higher wattage models toast faster and thus produce softer toast.

Toaster ovens were discussed in the previous section under the heading "Broilers."

Coffee Maker, Automatic Drip (1000-1200 watts)

These appliances use the drip method of making coffee and thus require a fine grind of coffee. Most coffee manufactures supply an "automatic drip" grind coffee. The coffee maker boils the water and allows it to pass over the coffee; the brew flows through a filter into the server which is kept at serving temperature by a heater in the base. (See pages 226 and 227 for recipe.)

Ice Cream Freezer (120-200 watts)

The freezing container is available in 4, 5, and 6 quart size. The dasher and freezing container are powered by an electric motor. The freezing mixture is a blend of rock salt and chipped ice. Refer to the chapter on Crystallization: Water (Desserts) for recipes and procedures (page 242).

Fondue Pots (800 watts)

Fondue pots are of 1 1/2-2 quart capacity, many are Teflon® coated. Cheese fondues are heated at low to medium temperatures. Meat fondues are heated to higher temperatures.

Chafing Dish

The chafing dish or blazer is used to cook food at the table. It is usually heated over a water bath but may be heated over direct heat. Most foods prepared in a chafing dish are flamed during the cooking process. Chafing dishes are most usually heated with sterno.

The WOK (1000 watts)

This style of cooking is referred to as "flash cooking." The cooking pan and the method of cutting the food are designed so the food will cook rapidly.

Two styles of WOKS are available. The original "Oriental" style is a shallow pan with slightly sloped sides; the heat is applied evenly to the inner 1/3 to 1/2 of the pan. The outer edges are thus slightly cooler than the center.

The newer electric WOKS have a recessed area in the bottom (approximately 6-7" in diameter and 1 1/2" deep). The heating coil is directly under this well. The sides slope up gradually from this well and are cooler than the center (heated) portion. The best electric WOKS are Teflon® coated.

In both types, the rate of cooking can be controlled by pulling the cooked food up on the cooler portions of the pan with a large spoon or spatula. A lid is provided for most WOKS.

Some recipes do not call for added water and are essentially a dry-heat method of cooking while other recipes have water added, have the lid in place, and are thus moist-heat cooking methods.

This same type of cooking may be done in a Teflon® coated electric fry pan and is referred to as stir-fry.

Recipes for WOK cooking are given on pages 141 and 180.

TIME SAVING EQUIPMENT

Two appliances must be mentioned in this classification, the Microwave Oven and the Pressure Cooker. One of the primary advantages of both of these appliances is time saving; for example, a 12 pound turkey can be roasted in about half the time required in a regular oven and a veal tongue can be cooked in 30 minutes in a pressure cooker, whereas it would take 2 1/2-3 hours to simmer it on the range. In both of these examples the quality of the product cooked more rapidly is the same as that of the product prepared by the conventional method.

Slicing Knife (100 watts)
This knife makes it easier to slice hot or cold meat but it will also cut cakes without crushing. It can also be used to cut a large variety of foods. The knife has 2 scallop-edged blades that do not require sharpening.

Electric Mixers (portable, 120 watts; standing, 150 watts)
There are two types of mixers, the standing mixer (mounted on a stand) and the portable mixer. The standing mixer has a heavy duty motor and can accomplish all types of mixing from bread doughs to beating egg whites. The portable mixer usually does not have the power to do heavy mixing. Both types have variable speed motors.

Many of the newer models have solid state controls which will keep the speed of the blades constant regardless of the thickness or viscosity of the food being mixed.

Blenders (720 watts)
This is an extremely versatile appliance; it has blending speeds from 2-16. It can accomplish a wide range of operations: it can crumb dry products, grate, chop, pulverize, mix, homogenize, mince, puree, liquefy, and form emulsions; all done faster and with less physical work than by hand. It does not replace the mixer or food grinder.

Food Processor (690 watts)
This is one of the newest appliances on the market and the price has come down sufficiently to make it available to many consumers. It is a versatile appliance which can perform many operations: mix, blend, crumb, slice, beat, emulsify, grate, knead, mash, julienne, cut French fries, crinkle cut, extract fruit juice, and whip. It is most efficient when large quantities are required, but it can also be used to process foods in daily food preparation. It can process all foods from almonds to zucchini.

It does take some time and experience to use it properly—used incorrectly it can be a "food surpriser".

Appendix A
(Evaluation Sheets)

EVALUATION OF PRODUCTS

Name: _____

Date: _____

Score System

Points	Quality
7	Excellent
6	Very good
5	Good
4	Medium
3	Fair
2	Poor
1	Very poor

Directions:
1. Place the numerical score in the box in the upper left hand corner.
2. Comments should justify the numerical score. Comments must be brief.
3. Evaluation of the food products must be on an *individual* basis.

Products

Quality Characteristic					
Appearance					
Consistency or Texture					
Tenderness					
Flavor					
Overall Eating Quality					

EVALUATION OF PRODUCTS

Name: _____

Date: _____

Score System

Points	Quality
7	Excellent
6	Very good
5	Good
4	Medium
3	Fair
2	Poor
1	Very poor

Directions:

1. Place the numerical score in the box in the upper left hand corner.
2. Comments should justify the numerical score. Comments must be brief.
3. Evaluation of the food products must be on an *individual* basis.

Products

Quality Characteristic					
Appearance					
Consistency or Texture					
Tenderness					
Flavor					
Overall Eating Quality					

EVALUATION OF PRODUCTS

Name: _____

Date: _____

Directions:

1. Place the numerical score in the box in the upper left hand corner.
2. Comments should justify the numerical score. Comments must be brief.
3. Evaluation of the food products must be on an *individual* basis.

Score System

Points	Quality
7	Excellent
6	Very good
5	Good
4	Medium
3	Fair
2	Poor
1	Very poor

Products

Quality Characteristic					
Appearance					
Consistency or Texture					
Tenderness					
Flavor					
Overall Eating Quality					

EVALUATION OF PRODUCTS

Name: _____

Date: _____

Score System

Points	Quality
7	Excellent
6	Very good
5	Good
4	Medium
3	Fair
2	Poor
1	Very poor

Directions:
1. Place the numerical score in the box in the upper left hand corner.
2. Comments should justify the numerical score. Comments must be brief.
3. Evaluation of the food products must be on an *individual* basis.

Products

Quality Characteristic					
Appearance					
Consistency or Texture					
Tenderness					
Flavor					
Overall Eating Quality					

EVALUATION OF PRODUCTS

Name: _____

Date: _____

Score System

Points	Quality
7	Excellent
6	Very good
5	Good
4	Medium
3	Fair
2	Poor
1	Very poor

Directions:

1. Place the numerical score in the box in the upper left hand corner.
2. Comments should justify the numerical score. Comments must be brief.
3. Evaluation of the food products must be on an *individual* basis.

Products

Quality Characteristic					
Appearance					
Consistency or Texture					
Tenderness					
Flavor					
Overall Eating Quality					

273

EVALUATION OF PRODUCTS

Name: _____

Date: _____

Score System

Points	Quality
7	Excellent
6	Very good
5	Good
4	Medium
3	Fair
2	Poor
1	Very poor

Directions:

1. Place the numerical score in the box in the upper left hand corner.
2. Comments should justify the numerical score. Comments must be brief.
3. Evaluation of the food products must be on an *individual* basis.

Products

Quality Characteristic					
Appearance					
Consistency or Texture					
Tenderness					
Flavor					
Overall Eating Quality					

EVALUATION OF PRODUCTS

Name: _____

Date: _____

Score System

Points	Quality
7	Excellent
6	Very good
5	Good
4	Medium
3	Fair
2	Poor
1	Very poor

Directions:
1. Place the numerical score in the box in the upper left hand corner.
2. Comments should justify the numerical score. Comments must be brief.
3. Evaluation of the food products must be on an *individual* basis.

Products

Quality Characteristic					
Appearance					
Consistency or Texture					
Tenderness					
Flavor					
Overall Eating Quality					

277

EVALUATION OF PRODUCTS

Name: _____

Date: _____

Score System

Points	Quality
7	Excellent
6	Very good
5	Good
4	Medium
3	Fair
2	Poor
1	Very poor

Directions:

1. Place the numerical score in the box in the upper left hand corner.
2. Comments should justify the numerical score. Comments must be brief.
3. Evaluation of the food products must be on an *individual* basis.

Products

Quality Characteristic					
Appearance					
Consistency or Texture					
Tenderness					
Flavor					
Overall Eating Quality					

EVALUATION OF PRODUCTS

Name: _____

Date: _____

Score System

Points	Quality
7	Excellent
6	Very good
5	Good
4	Medium
3	Fair
2	Poor
1	Very poor

Directions:

1. Place the numerical score in the box in the upper left hand corner.
2. Comments should justify the numerical score. Comments must be brief.
3. Evaluation of the food products must be on an *individual* basis.

Products

Quality Characteristic					
Appearance					
Consistency or Texture					
Tenderness					
Flavor					
Overall Eating Quality					

EVALUATION OF PRODUCTS

Name: _____

Date: _____

Score System

Points	Quality
7	Excellent
6	Very good
5	Good
4	Medium
3	Fair
2	Poor
1	Very poor

Directions:

1. Place the numerical score in the box in the upper left hand corner.
2. Comments should justify the numerical score. Comments must be brief.
3. Evaluation of the food products must be on an *individual* basis.

Products

Quality Characteristic					
Appearance					
Consistency or Texture					
Tenderness					
Flavor					
Overall Eating Quality					

EVALUATION OF PRODUCTS

Name: _____

Date: _____

Score System

Points	Quality
7	Excellent
6	Very good
5	Good
4	Medium
3	Fair
2	Poor
1	Very poor

Directions:

1. Place the numerical score in the box in the upper left hand corner.
2. Comments should justify the numerical score. Comments must be brief.
3. Evaluation of the food products must be on an *individual* basis.

Products

Quality Characteristic					
Appearance					
Consistency or Texture					
Tenderness					
Flavor					
Overall Eating Quality					

EVALUATION OF PRODUCTS

Name: _____

Date: _____

Score System

Points	Quality
7	Excellent
6	Very good
5	Good
4	Medium
3	Fair
2	Poor
1	Very poor

Directions:

1. Place the numerical score in the box in the upper left hand corner.
2. Comments should justify the numerical score. Comments must be brief.
3. Evaluation of the food products must be on an *individual* basis.

Products

Quality Characteristic					
Appearance					
Consistency or Texture					
Tenderness					
Flavor					
Overall Eating Quality					

EVALUATION OF PRODUCTS

Name: _____

Date: _____

Score System

Points	Quality
7	Excellent
6	Very good
5	Good
4	Medium
3	Fair
2	Poor
1	Very poor

Directions:

1. Place the numerical score in the box in the upper left hand corner.
2. Comments should justify the numerical score. Comments must be brief.
3. Evaluation of the food products must be on an *individual* basis.

Products

Quality Characteristic					
Appearance					
Consistency or Texture					
Tenderness					
Flavor					
Overall Eating Quality					

EVALUATION OF PRODUCTS

Name: _____

Date: _____

Score System

Points	Quality
7	Excellent
6	Very good
5	Good
4	Medium
3	Fair
2	Poor
1	Very poor

Directions:
1. Place the numerical score in the box in the upper left hand corner.
2. Comments should justify the numerical score. Comments must be brief.
3. Evaluation of the food products must be on an *individual* basis.

Products

Quality Characteristic					
Appearance					
Consistency or Texture					
Tenderness					
Flavor					
Overall Eating Quality					

291

EVALUATION OF PRODUCTS

Name: _____

Date: _____

Score System

Points	Quality
7	Excellent
6	Very good
5	Good
4	Medium
3	Fair
2	Poor
1	Very poor

Directions:

1. Place the numerical score in the box in the upper left hand corner.
2. Comments should justify the numerical score. Comments must be brief.
3. Evaluation of the food products must be on an *individual* basis.

Products

Quality Characteristic					
Appearance					
Consistency or Texture					
Tenderness					
Flavor					
Overall Eating Quality					

293

Appendix B
(Summary Outline Sheets)

SUMMARY OUTLINE: _____   *Name:* _____
(Product)   *Date:* _____

Summary Outlines emphasize application of principles to basic steps in preparation of a food product. Principles may have been discussed in lecture, in laboratory, or may have been in assigned readings. Include cooking or baking temperature and know *why* a low, medium, or high temperature is used. Summaries are excellent means for review.

List of Ingredients:

Steps in Preparation	*Principles Applied*
1.	1.

SUMMARY OUTLINE: _____   *Name:* _____
                                   (Product)   *Date:* _____

Summary Outlines emphasize application of principles to basic steps in preparation of a food product. Principles may have been discussed in lecture, in laboratory, or may have been in assigned readings. Include cooking or baking temperature and know *why* a low, medium, or high temperature is used. Summaries are excellent means for review.

List of Ingredients:

Steps in Preparation	Principles Applied
1.	1.

SUMMARY OUTLINE: _____ *Name:* _____

(Product)

Date: _____

Summary Outlines emphasize application of principles to basic steps in preparation of a food product. Principles may have been discussed in lecture, in laboratory, or may have been in assigned readings. Include cooking or baking temperature and know *why* a low, medium, or high temperature is used. Summaries are excellent means for review.

List of Ingredients:

Steps in Preparation	Principles Applied
1.	1.

SUMMARY OUTLINE: _____ _Name:_ _____
(Product) _Date:_ _____

Summary Outlines emphasize application of principles to basic steps in preparation of a food product. Principles may have been discussed in lecture, in laboratory, or may have been in assigned readings. Include cooking or baking temperature and know _why_ a low, medium, or high temperature is used. Summaries are excellent means for review.

List of Ingredients:

Steps in Preparation	Principles Applied
1.	1.

SUMMARY OUTLINE: _____   *Name:* _____

(Product)   *Date:* _____

Summary Outlines emphasize application of principles to basic steps in preparation of a food product. Principles may have been discussed in lecture, in laboratory, or may have been in assigned readings. Include cooking or baking temperature and know *why* a low, medium, or high temperature is used. Summaries are excellent means for review.

List of Ingredients:

Steps in Preparation	*Principles Applied*
1.	1.

Recipe Index

Apples
  baked, 190
  coddled, 189
  pie, 74
  sauce, 189
    microwaved, 254
Bacon
  microwaved, 254
  pan-broiled, 139
Beans
  blackeye, Southern sytle, 183
  kidney, curried, 184
  lima, barbecued, 185
  salad, 203
  stew, Western, 184
Beef
  patties
    microwaved, 254
    pan-broiled, 141
  steak, Swiss, 147
Beets, Harvard, 178
Beverages
  chocolate, 229
  cocoa, 229
  coffee, 226–227
  tea, 228
Biscuits
  baking powder, 30
  buttermilk, 30
Broccoli
  microwaved, 256
  with cheese sauce, 177
Cabbage
  cole slaw, 204
  red, sweet-sour, 178
Caesar salad, 205
Cakes
  angel, 125
  butter-type
    devil's food, 49
    plain, 47–48
  jelly roll, 127
  sponge, 126
Candies
  amorphous
    caramels, 236
    lollipops, 238
    peanut brittle, 237

  crystalline
    fudge
      chocolate, 233
      divinity, 235
      penuchi, 234
Caramels, 236
Cauliflower with cheese sauce, 177
Cereals, cooked, 99
Cheese
  sandwiches, grilled, 115
  sauce, microwaved, 251
  souffle, 128
Chef's salad, 206
Chicken
  breasts
    fried, 140
    pan-baked, 142
  salad, 207
  shrimp and vegetable, Japanese style, 143
  thighs, 146
Chocolate beverage, 229
Chocolate mousse with almonds, 243
Cocoa beverage, 229
Coffee, methods of preparation, 226–227
Cranberries, 190–191
Cream puffs, 58
Croutons, seasoned, 205
Custards
  baked, 118
    microwaved, 252
  stirred, 118
    microwaved, 253
Doughnut holes, 85
Eggs and egg foam products
  custards
    baked, 118
      microwaved, 252
    stirred, 118
      microwaved, 253
  floating island, 130
    microwaved, 253
  foam cakes, 125–126
  fried, 120
  hard-cooked, 120
  jelly roll, 127
  meringue, 130
    microwaved, 253
  omelet, 122

prune whip, baked, 127
scrambled, 121
  microwaved, 252
souffle, cheese, 128
Eggplant, pan-fried, 179
Fish and shellfish
  fillets or steaks, "oven-fried," 160
  finnan haddie, poached, 161
  perch, pan-fried, 159
  salmon steak, broiled, 160
  sauces to accompany, 163
  scallops, baked, 161
  shrimp, 159
  tuna salad, 207
  whole, baked, 162
Floating island, 130
  microwaved, 253
Fritters, 87
Fruit
  apples
    baked, 190
    coddled, 189
    sauce, 189
      microwaved, 254
  cranberries, 190–191
  pies
    apple, 74
    cherry, 74
  prunes
    plain, 192
    whip, baked, 129
  salad dressing, 213
  salads, 203, 208
    frozen, 209
Fudge
  chocolate, 233
  divinity, 235
  penuchi, 234
Gelatin products
  apricot sponge, 219
  lemon sponge, 219
  lime Bavarian, 221
  orange foam, 216
  orange jelly, 216
  perfection salad, 217
  pineapple Bavarian cream, 220
  reception salad, 218
  Spanish cream, 220
  strawberry chiffon, 221
  tomato aspic, 217
Ice cream
  chocolate, 242
  strawberry, 242
  vanilla, 242
Jelly roll, 127
Lamb
  curry, 150
  stew, 151

Legumes
  blackeye beans, Southern style, 183
  kidney beans, curried, 184
  lentils and rice with tomatoes, 183
  lima beans, barbecued, 185
  Western bean stew, 184
Liver, pan-broiled, 140
Lollipops, 238
Macaroni
  baked in tomatoe sauce, 102
  basic, 101
Mayonnaise dressing, 212
Meats
  bacon
    microwaved, 254
    pan-broiled, 139
  beef
    patties
      microwaved, 254
      pan-broiled, 141
    steak, Swiss, 147
  lamb
    curry, 150
    stew, 151
  liver, pan-broiled, 140
  pork
    chops, braised, 146
    chop suey, 141
  veal
    chops, breaded, braised, 147
    rosemary, braised, 149
    tongue, spiced, 148
Meringue, 130
  microwaved, 254
Microwaved products
  applesauce, 254
  bacon, 254
  beef patties, 254
  egg products
    custard
      baked, 252
      stirred, 253
    floating island, 253
    meringue, 253
    scrambled, 252
  muffins, cinnamon-sugar, 250
  starch products
    cheese sauce, 251
    chocolate pudding, 251
    white sauce, 250
  vegetables
    broccoli
      fresh, 256
      frozen, 256
    potato, baked, 255
    spinach, savory, 255
Muffins
  microwaved, 250

plain, 22
Mush
  corn meal, 99
  fried, 99
Noodles
  basic, 101
  with hamburger, 101
Onions, sauteed, 140
Orange milk sherbet, 244
Parsnips, fried, 179
Pasta
  cooking, 101
  macaroni baked in tomato sauce, 102
  noodles with hamburger, 101
  spaghetti with meat sauce, 102
Peanut brittle, 237
Perch, pan-fried, 159
Pie
  apple, 74
  cherry, 74
  cream, 134
Pie pastry
  double crust, 73
  single crust, 72
Popovers, 59
Pork
  chops, braised, 146
  chop suey, 141
Potatoes
  baked, 172
    microwaved, 255
  salad, hot, 206
Prunes
  plain fruit, 192
  prune whip, baked, 129
Puddings, starch
  chocolate, 94
    microwaved, 251
  creamy cornstarch, 135
  lemon, 134
  tapioca, 136
Rice
  basic, 100
  pilaf, 100
Salads
  appetizer
    five-bean, 203
    fruit, 203
    tomato, marinated, 204
  dessert
    fruit
      canned, 208
      fresh, 208
      frozen, 209
      reception, 218
  dinner accompaniment
    Caesar, 205
    coleslaw, 204

perfection, 217
  tomato aspic, 217
gelatin
  perfection, 217
  reception, 218
  tomato aspic, 217
main meal
  chef's, 206
  chicken, 207
  potato, hot, 206
  tuna, 207
Salad dressings
  French, 213
  fruit, 213
  honey-lemon-oil, 213
  mayonnaise, 212
Salmon steak, broiled, 160
Sauces
  cheese, microwaved, 251
  cocktail, 163
  drawn butter, 163
  tarter, 163
  white sauce, 93
    microwaved, 250
Scallops, baked, 161
Sherbet, orange milk, 244
Shrimp, 159
Souffle, cheese, 128
Soup, tomato, 109
Spaghetti
  basic, 101
  with meat sauce, 102
Spinach, savory, 178
  microwaved, 255
Swiss steak, 147
Tea, 228
Veal
  chops, breaded, braised, 147
  rosemary, braised, 149
  tongue, spiced, 148
Vegetables, cooked,
  beans
    blackeye, Southern style, 183
    kidney, curried, 184
    lima, barbecued, 185
    Western stew, 184
beets, Harvard, 178
boiling procedures, 170
broccoli
  microwaved, 256
  with cheese sauce, 177
buttered, 177
cabbage, red, sweet-sour, 178
cauliflower with cheese sauce, 177
creamed, 177
eggplant, pan-fried, 179
Japanese style, 180
lentils and rice with tomatoes, 183

onions, sauteed, 140
parsnips, fried, 179
potatoes
    baked, 172
        microwaved, 255
    salad, hot, 206
spinach, savory, 178

    microwaved, 255
    zucchini squash, fried, 180
White sauce, 93
    microwaved, 250
Yeast rolls, 38
Zucchini squash, fried, 180

Subject Index

Appliances, small, 260–263
  blender, 263
  broiler, 260
  casserole, 261
  chafing dish, 262
  coffee maker, automatic, 262
  convection oven, 261
  cooker-fryer, 260
  electric fry pan, 260
  fondue pot, 262
  food processor, 263
  griddle, 261
  ice cream freezer, 262
  microwave oven, 260
  mixer, 263
  pressure saucepan, 260
  roaster oven, 260
  slicing knife, 263
  slow cooker, 260
  toaster, 260, 262
  waffle baker/sandwich grill, 261
  WOK, 262
Baked products, descriptive terms, 20
Basic terms and concepts, 19
Browning
  caramelization, 21, 37
  dextrinization, 21, 37
  enzymatic, 71, 187–188
  Maillard reaction, 21, 37
  mechanisms in baked products, 21, 37
  milk, 104–109
Cheese
  natural, 110–115
  process, 110–115
Characteristics of high quality
  alimentary pastes (pasta), 101
  amorphous candies, 236–238
  angel cakes, 125
  apple products
    baked, 190
    coddled, 189
    sauce, 189
  bacon, 139
  baking powder biscuits
    drop, 31
    kneaded, 31
  buttermilk biscuits, 31

beverages
  chocolate, 229
  cocoa, 229
  coffee, 227
  tea, 228
butter type cakes, 48
cakes
  angel, 125
  butter type
    devil's food, 49
    plain, 48
  jelly roll, 128
  sponge, 126
caramels, 236
cereals, cooked, 98
cheese sandwiches, open-faced,
    grilled, 115
cheese sauce, 181
cheese souffle, 128
chocolate beverage, 229
chocolate pudding, 92
cocoa beverage, 229
coffee beverage, 227
corn meal mush, fried, 99
cornstarch pudding
  chocolate, 92
  creamy (see starch-egg products), 136
cranberry products, 191
cream puffs, 58
crystalline candies, 234–235
custards
  baked, 118
  stirred, 119
devil's food cake, 49
doughnuts holes, 86
eggs
  custards
    baked, 118
    stirred, 119
  fried, 121
  hard-cooked, 120
  raw, 119
  scrambled, 121
fish, 157
floating island, 130
fritters, 87
fruit pies, 74

fruit salad dressing
    (see starch-egg products), 136
fudge, crystalline candies
    chocolate, 234
    divinity, 235
    penuchi, 234
gelatin
    foams (plain whips), 222
    foam combined with whipped cream,
        foam/egg white foam, 222
    jellies, 222
ice cream, 243
jelly roll, 128
legume products, 185
lemon pudding
    (see starch-egg products), 136
lollipops (hard candies), 238
mayonnaise dressing, 212
meat and poultry, 142
meringue, soft, 130
mousse, chocolate, 243
muffins, 22
omelet, 122
peanut brittle, 237
pie pastry, 72
popovers, 59
potatoes, baked
    sweet potatoes, 172
    white potatoes, 172
prunes, 192
prune whip, 129
rice, cooked, 100
salads, 209
sherbet, orange milk, 244
shrimp, cooked, 159
souffle, cheese, 128
soup, tomato, 109
sponge cake, 126
starch-egg products, 133–136
tapioca pudding
    (see starch-egg products), 136
tea beverage, 228
vegetables, cooked, 181
vegetable sauces
    cheese, 181
    vinegar, 181
    white sauce, 92
yeast rolls, 39
Coagulation
    cheese, 110–111
    chocolate, 225
    cocoa, 225
    eggs, 57, 117, 123
    eggs related to starch gelatinization, 133
    fish, 158
    gluten, 21
    meat, 137–138
    milk, 107–108

Crystallization
    sugar (candies), 231
    water (frozen desserts), 240
Egg
    as binder, 145, 147
    as clarifier, 215
    combined with starch, 133
    custards, 117–118
    foams, 123–124
Eggs, shell, 117, 119
Emulsifiers, 46, 57, 111–112, 211
Emulsions
    cake, butter type, 46
    cheese, 111
    cream puffs, 57
    salad dressings, 211
Enzymes
    fruit, 71, 187–188
    rennet, 104, 107
Evaluations of food products, 4–8
    baked products, descriptive terms, 20
Fats and oils
    composition characteristics, 67
    deep-fat frying, 83–84
    fat absorption, 84
    in meat, 137
    pie pastry, 71
    salad dressings, 211
    smoke point, 83
Fish, biology and storage, 157
Flakiness
    biscuits, 30
    pie pastry, 71
Flavor in
    beverages, 224–225
    fats and oils, 67
    starch products, 97
    vegetables, 168
Foams
    egg white, 123–124
    evaporated milk, 221
    gelatin, 215, 216, 218–220
    whipped cream, 220–221
Gelation
    eggs, 117
    gelatin, 215
    meat, 137–138
    milk, 104
Gluten structure
    cake flour, 45
    coagulation, 21, 71
    formation, 21
    ingredient effect, 45–46, 56
    kneading, 37
    manipulation effects, 45–46, 56, 71
    quality, 21
    soaking of, 71
Hydration
    dried fruits, 187

flour protein, 21
gelatin, 215
legumes, 182
starch, 57, 71, 89
Leavening
  acid-soda, 30–31, 47
  air, 46–47, 71, 123
  baking powder, 21
  manipulative effect, 46–47
  steam, 57, 71
  yeast, 37
Legumes
  hydration, 182
  pectic substances, 182
Marinades, salads, 202
Measurements
  equivalents, 11
  methods, 14
  principles, 13
Metric conversion, 9–10
Microwave cooking principles, 248–249
Milk
  browning, 104
  coagulation, 104, 107–108, 109
  composition, 105
Objectives of laboratory experiences, 1
Oils, see Fats and oils
Osmosis in fruits, 186, 192
Pectic substances
  fruits, 186–187
  legumes, 182
  vegetables, 168
Pigments
  cocoa, Dutch process, 225
  vegetables, 167
Polyphenols (tannins), 224
Proteins
  egg, 117, 122
  fish, 157–158
  gelatin, 215
  meat, connective tissue, 137–138, 145
  meat, muscle fiber, 137–138, 145
  milk and cheese, 104, 110–111
  wheat flour, 21
Review questions
  baked products, general, 26–28
  biscuits, 32
  beverages, 230
  cakes, butter type, 50
  candy, 239
  cereals, 103
  cheese, 116
  cream puffs, 60
  deep-fat frying, 88
  egg and egg foam products, 131–132

evaluation of foods, 18
fats, 68
fish and shellfish, 164
frozen desserts, 247
fruits, 199–200
gelatin, 223
legumes, dried, 185
measurements, 17–18
meats, 155–156
microwave cooking, 257
milk, 116
muffins, 26–28
oils, 68
paste products, 103
pie pastry, 75
popovers, 60
rice, 103
salad dressings, 214
salads, 210
sanitation, 18
shellfish, 164
starch products, 103
starch-egg combinations, 136
sugar cookery, 239
vegetables, 199–200
yeast rolls, 40
Salad principles, 201–202
Sanitation
  dishwashing, 2–3
  foodhandling, 2
Starch
  as buffer in milk, 104
Starch gelatinization
  effect of dextrinization, 91
  cereals, 97
  chocolate beverage, 225
  chocolate pudding, 94
  cocoa beverage, 224
  cream puffs, 57
  paste products, 94, 97
  potatoes, baked, 172
  principles, 89–90
  rice, 97
  starch-egg interaction, 133
  type of starch, 91
  vegetables, 168
Stir frying, 139, 180
Sugar
  gelatin gels, 215
  peptization, 21, 123–124
Tannins (polyphenols), 224
Tables of equivalents, 11
Temperatures used in food preparation, 12
WOK cooking, 139, 180
Yeast activity, 37